Example MATHEMATICS FOR GCSE

Higher Level

Ewart Smith MSc

Head of Mathematics Department
Tredegar Comprehensive School

Stanley Thornes (Publishers) Ltd

First published in 1987 by:
Stanley Thornes (Publishers) Ltd
Old Station Drive
Leckhampton
CHELTENHAM GL53 0DN
England

Reprinted 1988
Reprinted 1989 twice
Reprinted 1990 twice

British Library Cataloguing in Publication Data

Smith, Ewart
    Examples in mathematics for GCSE higher
    level.
    1. Mathematics—1961–
    I. Title
    510   QA39.2

    ISBN 0–85950–704–1

Typeset in 12pt Aldine by Tech-Set, Gateshead, Tyne & Wear.
Printed and bound in Great Britain at The Bath Press, Avon.

Contents

Preface

The aim of this book is to provide a reservoir of examples for fourth-year and fifth-year students studying for the higher level of the new GCSE examinations.

The book is divided into three parts:

PART 1 provides examples on individual topics and forms the basis of a fourth-year course.

PART 2 consists of 24 revision papers which, together with specimen papers and past papers, will be sufficient for the fifth year.

PART 3 gives 10 aural tests. It is not intended that the student works these independently. The teacher, or other adult or student, can read these to you. Do not spend more than about 20 seconds on each question. The tests are straightforward. Some questions ask for simple statements of fact, while most require calculations to be made. They are intended as an introduction to this type of test and do not necessarily indicate the degree of difficulty the students will meet when sitting external examinations. A calculator should not be used for this work.

My thanks are due to my colleague Allan Snelgrove BSc for checking the answers and making several useful suggestions.

Ewart Smith
1987

Part 1: Exercises

Basic Number Work

1 In this question write down the next two terms for each sequence:
   (a) 10, 21, 33, 46   (b) 4, 9, 16, 25
   (c) 5, −1, −7, −13   (d) 1, 8, 27, 64
   (e) $\frac{2}{3}, -\frac{3}{4}, \frac{4}{5}, -\frac{5}{6}$ (f) 100, 10, 1, 0.1
   (g) $3a, 6a, 9a, 12a$ (h) $1, 2a, 3a^2, 4a^3$

2 Find the reciprocal of each of these:
   (a) $\frac{1}{3}$ (b) $\frac{4}{7}$ (c) $-\frac{12}{13}$ (d) $1\frac{2}{5}$

3 Put the given numbers in order of size, smallest first:
   (a) 8.1, 8.07, 8.70, 8.107   (b) $\frac{5}{6}, \frac{19}{24}, \frac{3}{4}, \frac{2}{3}$
   (c) $0.46, \frac{2}{5}, \frac{1}{3}, \frac{7}{15}$ (d) $1\frac{1}{4}, 1.45, 1.26, 1\frac{2}{5}$

4 Put the given numbers in order of size, largest first:
   (a) $0.5, \frac{3}{5}, 0.58, \frac{4}{7}$ (b) $\frac{8}{3}, 2\frac{1}{2}, 2.64, 2\frac{5}{8}$
   (c) $2.1, \sqrt{6}, 2.5, \sqrt[3]{8}$ (d) $0.28, \frac{7}{32}, \frac{5}{16}, \frac{1}{4}$

5 Find the value of:
   (a) 2^4 (b) 9^{-1} (c) $8°$ (d) $(\frac{1}{2})^{-2}$
   (e) $(\frac{2}{3})^{-1}$ (f) 5^{-2} (g) $(\frac{1}{4})^{-1}$ (h) 3^{-3}

6 Find:
   (a) $1\frac{3}{5} + 2\frac{8}{15}$ (b) $5\frac{1}{2} - 2\frac{3}{4}$
   (c) $1\frac{1}{8} \times \frac{2}{3}$ (d) $1\frac{2}{7} \div \frac{2}{9}$
   (e) $(\frac{2}{5} \div \frac{1}{6}) + (\frac{1}{6} \times 1\frac{1}{2})$ (f) $1\frac{2}{5} \times 1\frac{1}{4} \div \frac{7}{16}$
   (g) $1\frac{1}{4} \div 4\frac{7}{8}$ (h) $(\frac{1}{2} + \frac{1}{3} + \frac{1}{4}) \times 1\frac{5}{13}$

7 Find:
   (a) 2.64 + 0.05   (b) 2.64 × 0.05
   (c) 2.65 ÷ 0.5   (d) 1.68 ÷ 42
   (e) 0.8 × 0.4   (f) 2.4 − 1.93
   (g) (30 × 0.05) ÷ 150   (h) (1.7 − 1.3) ÷ 0.8
   (i) 2.6(0.8 − 0.08) × 50   (j) 4.3 − 1.7 × 2.1

8 Write each of the following numbers correct to:
   (a) the nearest 10,   (b) two decimal places,
   (c) three significant figures.
   (i) 2937.474   (ii) 98.397   (iii) 5.0909
   (iv) 600.837

9 Estimate the value of:

(a) $\dfrac{42.68 \times 16.92}{34.98 \times 7.28}$

(b) $\dfrac{60.61}{3.142 \times 4.927}$

(c) 19.58^2

(d) $\dfrac{1}{4.97^2}$

(Do not use a calculator.)

10 Find, without using a calculator:
   (a) $7 - (-4)$ (b) $4 - 2 \times 3 + 8$
   (c) $(-2) \times 5$ (d) $9 \times (-3) + 2$
   (e) $(-5) \times (-2)$ (f) $(-12) \div (-4)$
   (g) $10 \div (-2)$ (h) $1 + 2 + 3 \times 4$

11 Express each of the following numbers as the product of its prime factors:
   (a) 225   (b) 420   (c) 546   (d) 1368

12 Express 1764 as the product of its prime factors, and hence find its square root.

13 (a) Divide 35 in the ratio $3:4$.
   (b) Divide 72 in the ratio $7:2$.
   (c) Divide £1.52 in the ratio $3:5$.
   (d) Divide 651 cm^3 in the ratio $2:5$.

14 Express the following numbers in standard form:
   (a) 4000   (b) 8 million
   (c) 0.073   (d) thirty-five thousand
   (e) 86 000   (f) half a million
   (g) 0.000 000 68   (h) 529.7

15 Simplify the following numbers, giving your answers in standard form:
   (a) $9.2 \times 10^3 \times 0.5 \times 10^4$ (b) $4.8 \times 10^6 \times 0.02 \times 10^3$
   (c) $36 \times 10^4 \div 0.6 \times 10^2$ (d) $2.3 \times 10^5 \times 2.1 \times 10^{-4}$
   (e) $0.04 \times 10^3 \div 2 \times 10^{-5}$ (f) $9.03 \times 10^{-4} \div 3 \times 10^{-6}$

Problems Involving Number Work 2

1 The distance of the Earth from the Sun is 93 million miles. Express this distance in standard form.

2 The distance from the Earth to the Sun is 150 million kilometres. Express this distance in standard form.

3 Light travels at a speed of 186 000 miles per second. How far will it travel in a year of 365 days? Give your answer in the form $a \times 10^n$ where a is correct to two significant figures.

4 A light year is the distance that light can travel in a year. If the speed of light is 1.85×10^5 miles per second how far, in miles, is one light year? How long would it take to travel this distance in Concorde if the aeroplane travels at 1400 m.p.h.?

5 The population of a country is estimated to double every 30 years. In 1900 it was 100 000.
(a) What was the population in 1960?
(b) When will the population be 1.6×10^6?
(c) When was the population $2^{\frac{1}{2}} \times 10^5$?
(d) What was the population in 1945?

Give your answers to (a) and (d) in standard form.

6 The length of a field is 85 metres correct to the nearest metre. Find the range in which the actual length lies.

7 At a recent international match at Wembley Stadium the recorded attendance was 87 489. Write this attendance correct to:
(a) the nearest thousand,   (b) the nearest hundred,
(c) three significant figures.

8 At their last home game the recorded attendance for Barcelona was 55 000, correct to the nearest thousand. Write down:
(a) the smallest number of people that could have been present,
(b) the largest number that could have been present.

9 An advertisement in *Stamp Weekly* says, '500 stamps (correct to the nearest 100) for £1.95'. What is the largest number of stamps you would expect to receive if you answered this advertisement? Ignore the stamps on the envelope!

4

10 Three ascending whole numbers form a Pythagorean triad when the square of the first number added to the square of the second number is equal to the square of the third number.

For example:

First triad	3	4	5
Second triad	5	12	13
Third triad	7	24	25
Fourth triad	9	40	41

Study the pattern found in these numbers and then answer the following questions:

(a) Write down the numbers in the fifth triad.

(b) Write down the numbers in the sixth triad.

(c) In the eighth triad, what number appears in the first column?

(d) If the third number in the eighth triad is 145, what is the second number?

(e) If the middle number in the ninth triad is 180, what are the other two numbers?

[Any multiple of any sets of the above numbers also give Pythagorean triads e.g. 3×4, 4×4, 5×4 i.e. 12, 16, 20 or 7×3, 24×3, 25×3 i.e. 21, 72, 75 but these are not considered 'basic' triads for the sake of this question.]

11 Any even number greater than four is the sum of two odd prime numbers. Express:

(a) 24   (b) 34   (c) 42   (d) 50   (e) 70

as the sum of two odd prime numbers.

12 The numbers given below form a part of Pascal's Triangle. Can you see a pattern in the numbers? Write down the next three lines.

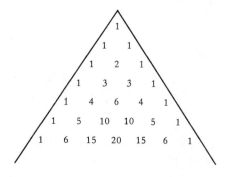

13 The numbers 1, 3, 6, 10, 15, 21, 28, are called triangular numbers. Write down the next three triangular numbers.

14 The numbers 1, 5, 12, 22, 35, are called pentagonal numbers. Write down the next two pentagonal numbers.

15

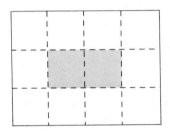

The diagram shows a pattern of two red tiles surrounded by ten white tiles.

(a) How many tiles are required to surround a row of:
   (i) 3 red tiles   (ii) 4 red tiles   (iii) 10 red tiles?

(b) How many white tiles are required to surround a row of n red tiles?

(c) Use your answer to (b) to find:
   (i) the number of white tiles required to surround a row of 60 red tiles,
   (ii) the number of red tiles surrounded by 490 white tiles.

16

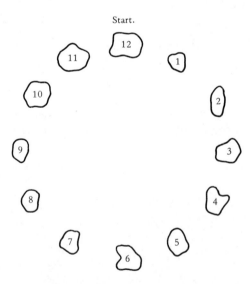

Twelve stepping stones are arranged in a circle and numbered 1 to 12 in a similar way to the numbers on the face of a clock.

Iona starts at the 12 and hops clockwise around the circle, stopping to change feet every time she has made five hops. She wishes to carry on hopping around the circle until she has stopped to change feet on every stone.

(a) (i) Is this possible?
    (ii) If it is, how many times must she go around the circle to do it?
    (iii) Which number is she on when she changes feet for the fourth time and for the last time?

(b) Iona next hops around the circle, stopping to change feet every time she had made three hops. Explain why, in this case, she will not stop at each one of the twelve stones, no matter how many times she hops around the circle.

(c) If Iona stops to change feet every time she has made x hops, for which values of x will she eventually stop to change feet on each of the twelve stones?

17

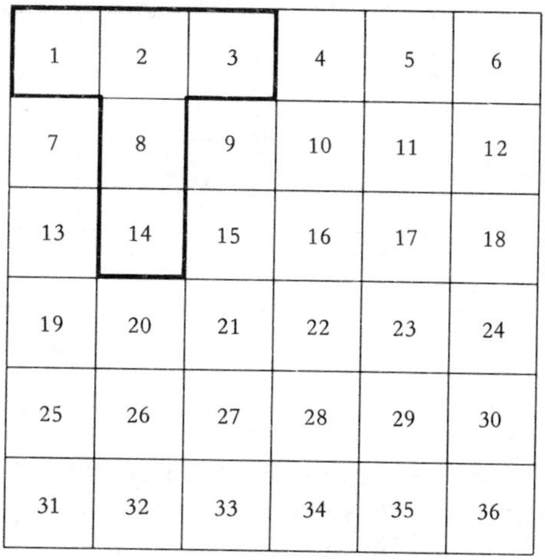

1	2	3	4	5	6
7	8	9	10	11	12
13	14	15	16	17	18
19	20	21	22	23	24
25	26	27	28	29	30
31	32	33	34	35	36

The diagram shows a number square with an outline T on it. The number at the base of the outline is 14 so we say that the outline is 'based on 14'. Using a translation, the outline can be moved so that it is based on a different number, but it must always remain upright and completely within the number square.

(a) Find the total of the five numbers within the outline when it is based on:
    (i) 20   (ii) 29.

(b) If the outline is based on x, find in terms of x, the other four numbers in the outline. Show that the total of all five numbers in the outline is $5x - 42$.

(c) Find the five numbers in the outline if they have a total of 118.

(d) Can the total of the five numbers be:
    (i) 158   (ii) 128   (iii) 78   (iv) 85?
Give reasons for your answers.

1	2	3	4	5
6	7	8	9	10
11	12	13	14	15
16	17	18	19	20
21	22	23	24	25
26	27	28	29	30
31	32	33	34	35
36	37	38	39	40
41	42	43	44	45
46	47	48	49	50

The diagram shows a number rectangle with a square marked on it. This is called 'the 26 square' because 26 is the number in the top left-hand corner of the square.

(a) Find the total of the numbers in:
   (i) the 42 square   (ii) the 29 square.

(b) Write down, in terms of x, the other three numbers in 'the x square', and show that the total of these four numbers is $4x + 12$.

(c) Which square has a total of:
   (i) 88   (ii) 168?

(d) What is the maximum total possible? What value of x gives this maximum?

(e) What is the minimum total possible? What value of x gives this minimum?

(f) Explain why the total of the four numbers in any square could not be:
   (i) 146   (ii) 212.

8

19

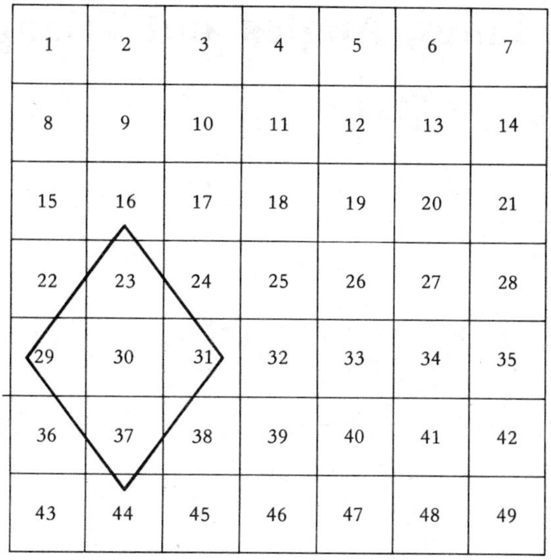

1	2	3	4	5	6	7
8	9	10	11	12	13	14
15	16	17	18	19	20	21
22	23	24	25	26	27	28
29	30	31	32	33	34	35
36	37	38	39	40	41	42
43	44	45	46	47	48	49

The diagram shows a number square with a rhombus marked on it. It is called the '30 rhombus' since 30 is the central number.

(a) Write down the numbers in the '20 rhombus'.

(b) Write down the sum of the numbers in the '17 rhombus'.

(c) Write down the numbers in the 'n' rhombus if:
   (i) n is as small as possible,
   (ii) n is as large as possible.

(d) Write down, in terms of n, the sum of the numbers in the 'n rhombus'.

(e) Which rhombus has a total of 200?

(f) Could the total be:
   (i) 85   (ii) 107   (iii) 70?

Give reasons for your answers.

20 A football league is to be reduced from 22 teams to 18 teams.

(a) How many fewer matches would need to be played by each of the remaining teams, assuming that any two teams play matches against each other both at home and away?

(b) If each team plays on average twice a week, by how many weeks will the season be shortened?

(c) In total, how many fewer league matches will there be?

Parallel Lines, Angles and Triangles   **3**

Find the angles marked with letters:

1

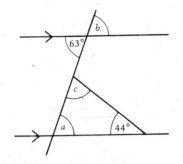

2

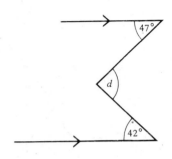

3

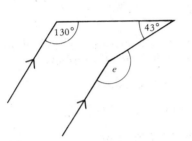

4

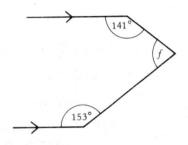

5

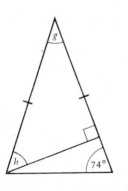

6

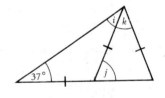

7

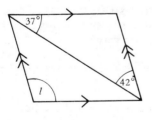

8

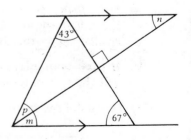

9

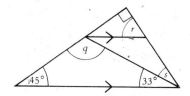

10

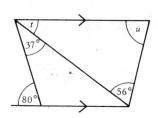

11

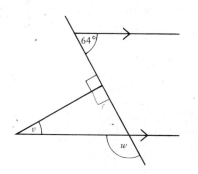

12

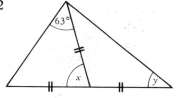

13

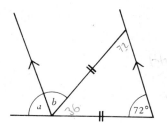

14

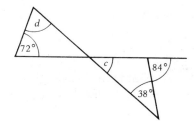

15

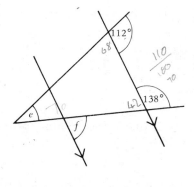

16

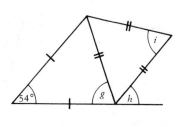

Polygons

1 Find (a) the exterior angle (b) the interior angle, of a regular polygon with:

    (i) five sides,   (ii) six sides,   (iii) eight sides,

    (iv) nine sides,   (v) ten sides,   (vi) twelve sides,

  (vii) twenty-four sides.

2 Fill in the blanks in the following table which gives the connection between the interior angle, the exterior angle and the number of sides for various regular polygons.

Number of sides	Exterior angle	Interior angle
...	45°	...
...	...	150°
18	...	...
20	...	...
...	15°	...
...	...	156°

3 Is it possible to have a regular polygon with an exterior angle of:

  (a) 20°   (b) 30°   (c) 40°   (d) 50°?

4 A pentagon has angles $x°$, $(x + 20)°$, $(x + 52)°$, $(x - 9)°$ and $(x + 12)°$. Find x.

5

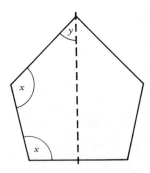

The diagram shows a pentagon with just one axis of symmetry. Find the angles of the pentagon when y is 44°.

6 ABCDEF is a regular hexagon. Calculate the angles of triangle ABE.

7

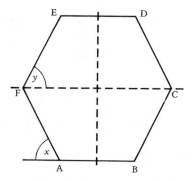

ABCDEF is a hexagon with just two axes of symmetry. Find all the interior angles when x is $37°$.

8   An octagon has four equal angles, each of size $x°$, two angles of size $(x + 30)°$, one of size $(x + 120)°$ and one of size $(x + 12)°$. Find x.

9

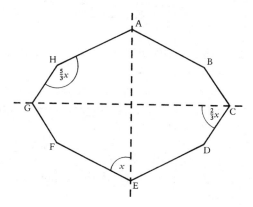

The diagram shows an octagon with just two axes of symmetry. Find x.

10   If ABCDE is a regular pentagon show that the straight lines EB and EC trisect the angle AED.

11   ABCDEF is a regular hexagon. Find the obtuse angle between the lines AD and BE.

12   A regular pentagon ABCDE and an equilateral triangle ABF lie on opposite sides of AB. Calculate the angles of triangle ADF.

13   In an octagon each angle except one is $10°$ greater than the angle next to it in a clockwise direction. Find the size of:
   (a) the smallest angle,   (b) the largest angle.

13

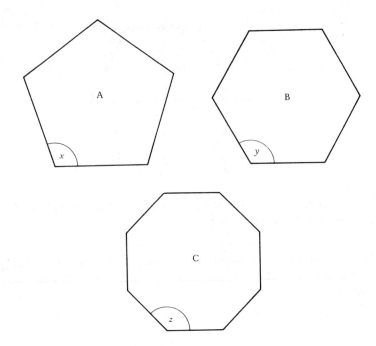

The drawings show three different tiles, A, B and C, each in the shape of a regular polygon.

(a) Calculate the size of the angles marked x, y and z.

(b) Which of these tiles fit together to cover a floor without any gaps between them?

15 The size of each exterior angle of a regular polygon is $x°$ and the size of each interior angle is $5x°$. Find the value of x and the number of sides of the polygon.

Scale Drawings   5

1 From a ship (S) the distance and bearing of a lighthouse (L) is 500 m in a direction N33°E, and the distance and bearing of a trawler (T) is 750 m in a direction S57°E. Taking 2 cm ≡ 100 m make a scale drawing and use it to find the distance and bearing of the lighthouse from the trawler.

2 From a point 160 m from the base of a church tower the angles of elevation of the base and top of the spire are 32° and 46° respectively. Make a scale drawing using 1 cm ≡ 10 m and use it to find the height of the spire.

3   Standing at one corner A of a triangular field the other two corners B and C are 132 m in a direction N40°W and 94 m in a direction N55°E respectively. Draw a plan of the field taking 1 cm ≡ 10 m and use it to find:

(a) the distance BC,   (b) the bearing of C from B.

4   Viewed from the top of a cliff 45 metres high the angles of depression of two boats directly out to sea are 42° and 29°. Using 1 cm ≡ 5 m make a scale drawing and use it to find:

(a) the distance of each boat from the base of the cliff,

(b) the distance between the boats.

5   Make an accurate scale drawing of a parallelogram ABCD in which AB is 74 cm, AD is 62 cm and $B\widehat{A}D$ is 65°. Use a scale of 1 cm to represent 10 cm.

Use your drawing to find the lengths of the diagonals of the parallelogram.

6   A field is in the shape of a quadrilateral ABCD in which AB = 100 m, BC = 70 m, BD = 140 m, $A\widehat{B}C$ = 110° and $B\widehat{C}D$ = 100°.

Using a scale of 1 cm to represent 10 m make an accurate scale drawing of the field.

Use your diagram to find:

(a) the lengths of AD and DC,

(b) the angle $A\widehat{D}C$.

7   An aeroplane takes off from an airfield and follows the following route: 50 km N37°E, 40 km S25°E, 150 km S37°E. Draw a scale diagram taking 1 cm ≡ 10 km, and use it to find the bearing it must set to return to its starting point, and the time it will take if it flies at 500 km/h.

8   A cross-country course starts at the clubhouse, takes a south easterly path for 4.5 km, changes direction to N38°E for 7.5 km before running due N for 3 km. The direction then changes yet again to N70°W for 10 km. Taking 1 cm ≡ 1 km make a plan of the route. Hence find the distance and bearing of the clubhouse from the point where a runner finally turns for home.

15

9   The diagram shows the position of a house within a plot of ground
    ABCD. Using a scale of 1 cm to 2 m draw an accurate plan. Hence
    find:

    (a) the lengths of the diagonals of the plot,

    (b) the distance from D to the nearest point of the house.

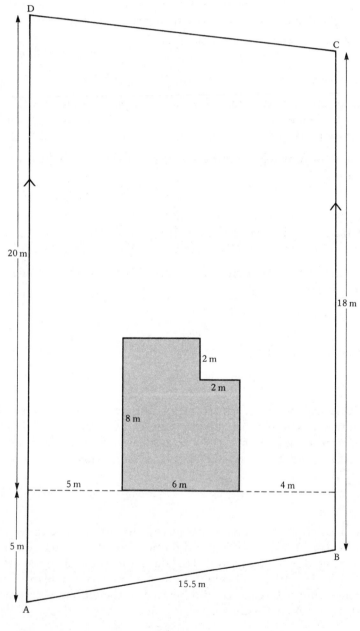

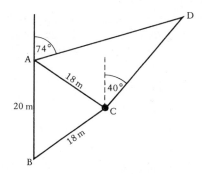

A and B show the positions of the wickets, which are 20 m apart, on a cricket pitch. The batsman at A strikes the ball towards D where AD makes an angle of 74° with the line of the wickets BA. A fielder standing at C, which is 18 m from each wicket, runs along the path CD in order to cut off the shot – CD making an angle of 40° with the direction BA. If the fielder intercepts the ball at D make a scale drawing and from it find:

(a) the distance the fielder runs before he retrieves the ball,

(b) the distance travelled by the ball along the ground from bat to hand. (Use 1 cm ≡ 2 m.)

Percentages 6

1 A builders' merchant allows a discount of $2\frac{1}{2}\%$ for cash sales. What would be the cash price of goods marked at £480?

2 The fashion department in a large store gives a 25% discount on a particular line of dresses during the summer sale. How much would Irene have to pay for a dress marked £68?

3 A video recorder costs £240 after a discount of 20% has been allowed. What was the marked price?

4 If 45% of the pupils in a school go home to lunch and 792 stay in school for lunch, how many pupils are there in total?

5 A joint of meat loses 8% of its weight when thawed. If a piece of lamb weighs 2.5 kg when taken out of the freezer, what does it weigh when thawed out?

6 A retailer buys 30 boxes of strawberries at 35p each and sells 28 of them at 30% profit. If the remaining two boxes are thrown away, how much profit does he make?

7 In 1987 a family of four spent a holiday in Brittany. The cost was divided as follows: 60% of the total was spent on hotel bills, 25% on travelling, and the remainder on general expenses. The hotel bills came to £490.80. Find:

(a) the total cost of the holiday,

(b) the amount spent on travelling,

(c) the amount spent on general expenses.

8 A shopkeeper marks a three-piece suite at £800. If he allows a discount of 10% on the marked price he still makes a profit of £240. Find his percentage profit if he sells at the marked price.

9 On a certain Monday morning 756 women reported for work at a factory. This was 84% of the total workforce. How many women were absent?

10 Between 1977 and 1987 car prices increased by 290% while petrol prices increased by 110%. A woman bought a car in 1977 for £4200 when the price of petrol was 95p per gallon. How much would she expect to pay for the car in 1987? What would be the price of petrol in 1987?

11 A motor car is bought for £12000 and depreciates by 25% of its value the first year, 20% the second year and 10% each year after the second. Find its value:

(a) after 2 years,   (b) after 4 years.

12 The value of a house increases by 10% each year. If a house is bought for £50000 what is its value after 4 years? Give your answer correct to the nearest thousand pounds.

13 When the price of a pair of shoes is reduced by 20% they are sold for £22.40. Find the original price.

14 An estate agent charges 2% commission on the value of a house. What are his charges for a house selling at £48000?

15 A dining suite is offered for sale at £750. If cash is paid, a discount of $2\frac{1}{2}$% is given, but if it is bought on hire purchase, the terms are: 20% deposit plus 24 monthly payments of £31.36. Find the amount saved by paying for the suite in cash rather than using hire purchase.

16 The price of a light fitting increases by 96p when the rate of VAT is increased from 15% to 18%. Find the original price of the light fitting excluding VAT.

17 Find the simple interest on £434 invested for 5 years at 8%.

18 How long must £420 be invested at 8% p.a. simple interest to increase in value by £134.40?

19 What annual rate of simple interest is necessary to give interest of £504 on a principal of £1200 invested for 6 years?

18

20 Find the compound interest on £360 for 2 years at 8%. Give your answer correct to the nearest penny.

21 Find the compound interest on £536 for 3 years at $10\frac{1}{2}$%. Give your answer correct to the nearest penny.

22 A rare postage stamp increases in value by 15% each year. If its value now is £80 what will it be worth in 3 years time? Give your answer correct to the nearest £5.

23 Bill Beeks is left with a weekly income of £119.60 after deductions, which amount to 35% of his gross wage, have been made. Find his gross wage.

24 The telephone rental for domestic users is £20.50 per quarter. Calls are metered in units of time, each unit costing 5p. Find the cost of the telephone for a quarter when 245 units are recorded. In addition, 15% value added tax is added to the total. Find the amount payable.

25 A tumble dryer is bought on hire purchase. A deposit of 20% of the cash price of £140 is required together with 24 monthly payments of £6.30. Find the extra cost using hire purchase. Express this as a percentage of the cash price.

26 A couple decide to buy a house priced at £27 200. A building society is prepared to advance 80% of the purchase price. The monthly repayments are at the rate of 95p per £100 borrowed over a period of 20 years.
   (a) What is the amount borrowed?
   (b) What is the total cost of the house?

27 The gross insurance premium per year for a motor bike is £480. After one year a discount of 20% is allowed, after two years 40%, after three years 50%, and for each year after the third 60%. A boy insures his bike over a five-year period. Calculate the total he pays in premiums.

28 A salesman receives a basic wage of £20 per week, together with commission of 3% of the total value of his sales. How much does he earn in a week when he sells goods to the value of £5200?

29 Is milk sold at 36p per litre more expensive than milk sold at 20p per pint? (1 litre = $1\frac{3}{4}$ pints.)

30 An estate agent charges $1\frac{1}{2}$% on the first £12 000 of the selling price of a house, and 1% thereafter. Calculate his charges on a house selling at £42 000.

31 If a sewing machine, marked at £324, is bought for cash, a discount of $2\frac{1}{2}$% is allowed. If it is bought on hire purchase, the terms are: one third deposit plus 18 monthly payments of £14.25. How much is saved by paying cash?

32　The gross insurance premium for a motor-cycle is £269 p.a. If 60% of this premium is deducted under 'no-claims bonus' and 20% of the *balance* is deducted because the insured agrees to pay the first £100 of each and every claim, calculate the net annual premium.

33　A microwave oven may be bought at the cash price of £212.50 or on hire purchase by paying a deposit of 30% and 24 monthly payments of £7.13. Find the extra paid by using hire purchase and express this as a percentage of the cash price, giving your answer correct to the nearest whole number.

34　A business machines salesman receives a basic wage of £95 per month plus commission. His commission is calculated as follows:

$$
\begin{array}{ll}
\text{On the first } \pounds 20\,000 & \text{nil} \\
\text{On the next } \pounds 10\,000 & 1\frac{1}{2}\% \\
\text{On the remainder} & 2\%
\end{array}
$$

Find his income in a month when he sells machines to the value of £46 260.

35　An importer buys 100 sets of instruments in West Germany for 1800 Deutschmarks. Find the price he must sell at in the United Kingdom if he is to make a profit of 35%. If value added tax increases the price by a further 20%, what is the price per set to the customer? (2.5 DM ≡ £1.)

36　A refrigerator, marked at £155, may be bought on hire purchase or for cash. If it is bought on HP the terms are 20% deposit plus 23 monthly repayments of £6.20. A cash sale results in a discount of 5%. Calculate the difference in the two prices.

Indices　　　　　　　　　　　　　　　　　　7

Simplify:

1 (a) $9^{\frac{1}{2}}$	(b) $9^{-\frac{1}{2}}$	(c) 3^{-2}	(d) $27^{-\frac{2}{3}}$
2 (a) $4^{\frac{1}{2}}$	(b) 4^{-1}	(c) 4^{0}	(d) 4^{-2}
3 (a) $16^{\frac{1}{4}}$	(b) $16^{\frac{1}{2}}$	(c) $4^{\frac{3}{2}}$	(d) $32^{\frac{1}{5}}$
4 (a) $8^{\frac{1}{3}}$	(b) $8^{\frac{4}{3}}$	(c) $8^{-\frac{4}{3}}$	(d) $16^{-\frac{3}{4}}$
5 (a) $125^{\frac{1}{3}}$	(b) $125^{\frac{2}{3}}$	(c) 25^{0}	(d) 5^{-3}
6 (a) 2^{-2}	(b) 20^{0}	(c) $64^{\frac{2}{3}}$	(d) $32^{\frac{2}{5}}$
7 (a) $49^{\frac{3}{2}}$	(b) $49^{-\frac{1}{2}}$	(c) $343^{\frac{1}{3}}$	(d) 7^{-2}
8 (a) $9^{\frac{3}{2}}$	(b) $9^{\frac{3}{2}} \times 9^{-1}$	(c) $(9^{\frac{1}{2}})^{2}$	(d) $9^{-\frac{3}{2}}$
9 (a) $4^{-\frac{3}{2}}$	(b) $(\frac{1}{4})^{2}$	(c) $(\frac{1}{4})^{-\frac{1}{2}}$	(d) $4^{-\frac{1}{2}}$

10 (a) $\frac{1}{10^2}$ (b) $100^{-\frac{1}{2}}$ (c) $10^0 \times 9^0$ (d) $(\frac{1}{100})^{-\frac{1}{2}}$

11 (a) 2×2^{-4} (b) $2^{\frac{1}{2}} \times 2^{-\frac{1}{2}}$ (c) $2^{-3} \times 4^{\frac{1}{2}}$ (d) $2^2 \div 2^{-2}$

12 (a) $3^{\frac{2}{3}} \times 3^{\frac{1}{3}}$ (b) $\frac{1}{3^{-3}}$ (c) $12^{\frac{1}{2}} \times 3^{\frac{1}{2}}$

13 (a) $2^3 \div 2^4$ (b) $16^{-\frac{3}{4}} \times 2^2$

14 (a) $2^{\frac{1}{3}} \times 3^{\frac{1}{3}} \times 6^{\frac{2}{3}}$ (b) $24^{\frac{2}{3}} \times 16^{\frac{1}{3}} \div 18^{\frac{1}{3}}$

15 (a) $a^2 \times a^3$ (b) $a^5 \times a^3$ (c) $a^5 \div a^2$ (d) $a^9 \div a^5$

16 (a) $x^{12} \div x^5$ (b) $\frac{x^4}{x^3}$ (c) $x^3 \times x^0$ (d) $x^7 \times x^5$

17 (a) $x^9 \div x^5$ (b) $x^4 \div x^{-2}$ (c) $x^5 \times x^{-2}$ (d) $(x^3)^2$

18 (a) $(x^{-2})^3$ (b) $(x^{-\frac{3}{4}})^0$ (c) $(3x)^2$ (d) $x^3 \times x^{\frac{1}{2}}$

19 (a) $x^3 \div x^{\frac{1}{2}}$ (b) $x^6 \times x^{-4}$ (c) $x^6 \div x^{-4}$ (d) $(4x)^{-2}$

20 (a) $a^2 \times a^3 \times a^{-5}$ (b) $\sqrt{a^3 \times a^5}$ (c) $\sqrt{9a^4b^2}$

21 Which two of these have the same value?
$$2^6, \quad 6^2, \quad 3^4, \quad 4^3$$

22 Which two of these have the same value?
$$4^{\frac{1}{2}}, \quad 4^{-\frac{1}{2}}, \quad 16^{\frac{1}{4}}, \quad 2^0$$

The Straight Line   8

1 For each of the following sketches find the equation of the straight line shown:

(a)
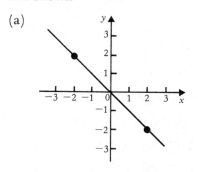

(b)
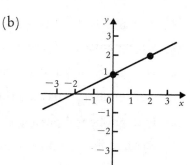

(*continued overleaf*)

(c)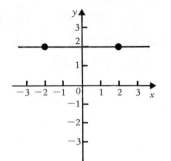

(d)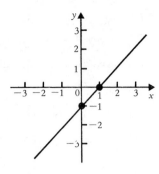

(e)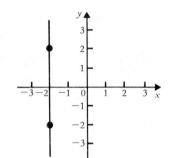

(f)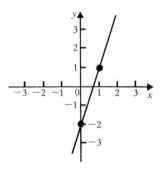

2   Find the gradient and y-intercept of the straight line with equation:

(a) $y = 4x + 3$ (b) $y = 5 - 3x$ (c) $3y = x + 2$

(d) $5y = 3x - 5$ (e) $3x + 2y - 4 = 0$ (f) $5x - 3y - 7 = 0$

3   Find the equation of the straight line:

(a) with gradient 2 and y-intercept 5,

(b) with gradient -1 and y-intercept 4,

(c) with gradient $\frac{1}{2}$ and y-intercept -3,

(d) with gradient $\frac{1}{2}$ passing through the point $(4, 5)$,

(e) with gradient 4 passing through the point $(-2, 6)$,

(f) passing through the points $(3, 0)$ and $(0, 4)$,

(g) passing through the points $(1, 2)$ and $(4, 8)$,

(h) passing through the points $(-2, 3)$ and $(5, 1)$.

4

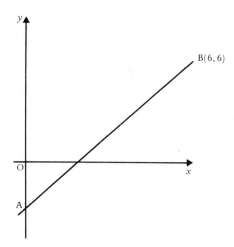

The gradient of AB is $\frac{4}{3}$. A lies on the y-axis and B is the point $(6,6)$.

(a) Find the coordinates of A.

(b) If the equation of AB is $y = mx + c$, write down the values of m and c.

(c) Calculate the distance AB.

5

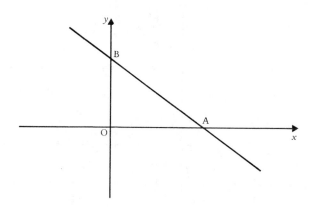

The straight line with equation $5x + 4y - 40 = 0$ cuts the x-axis at A and the y-axis at B.

(a) Find the coordinates of A.

(b) Find the coordinates of B.

(c) If the equation is re-written in the form $y = mx + c$ give the values of m and c.

6

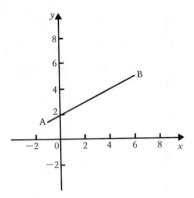

Given the points $A(-1, \frac{3}{2})$ and $B(6, 5)$ on the diagram, plot the points $C(-1, 4)$ and $D(2, 8)$. Join A to C, C to D and D to B. Complete the figure so that it is symmetrical about AB. If E is the reflection of D in the line AB and F is the reflection of C in the same line, write down the coordinates of E and F. What is the area of the completed figure?

7

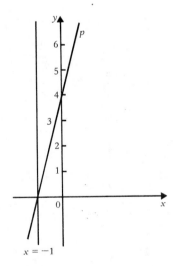

The line p meets the x-axis at the point $(-1, 0)$ and the y-axis at the point $(0, 4)$. When p is reflected in the line $x = -1$, its image is the line q.

(a) What is the gradient of p?

(b) Copy the diagram and draw the line q.

(c) What is the gradient of q?

(d) Write down the equation of q.

8

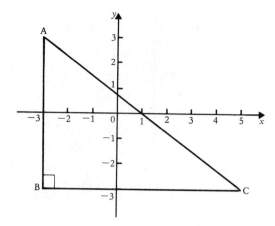

Copy this diagram on to squared paper. ABC is a right-angled triangle.

(a) Write down the coordinates of A, B and C.

(b) Write down the lengths of (i) AB (ii) BC. Measure the length of AC on your diagram.

(c) Can you use the lengths of AB and BC to calculate the length of AC? What is the calculated length of AC?

(d) What is the gradient of AC?

9

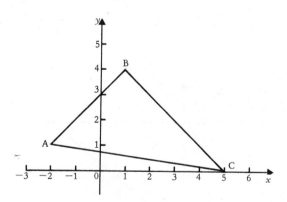

(a) Write down the coordinates of A, B and C.

(b) Find the gradient of AB and write down the coordinates of the point where the line AB crosses the y-axis. What is the equation of the line AB?

(c) Find the gradient of BC.

(d) What is the product of the gradients of AB and BC?

(e) Measure the lengths of AB, BC and AC, each correct to one decimal place. Find $AB^2 + BC^2$. How does this compare with the value of AC^2? What can you deduce about the value of angle ABC?

(f) Measure $A\widehat{B}C$.

(g) What is the area of triangle ABC?

10

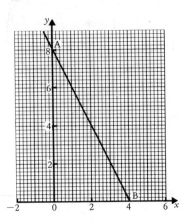

The graph shows part of the straight line AB which passes through the points $A(0, 8)$ and $B(4, 0)$. If the equation of this line is $y = mx + c$ find the value of m and the value of c.

By finding the values of y for $x = -2$, $x = 0$ and $x = 4$ draw the graph of $y = \frac{1}{2}x + 3$.

From your graph write down the coordinates of the point P where the two straight lines cross. On the graph shade the area bounded by

$$x > 0, \quad y > 0 \quad \text{and} \quad y < \tfrac{1}{2}x + 3$$

11

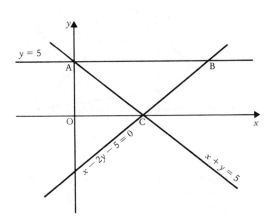

The diagram shows the graphs of the straight lines $x + y = 5$, $x - 2y - 5 = 0$ and $y = 5$.

(a) Find the coordinates of A, B and C.

(b) For the line $x - 2y - 5 = 0$ find the value of y when $x = 2$.

(c) Shade the area which satisfies all the inequalities:

$$x > 0, \quad x + y < 5, \quad x - 2y > 5$$

12

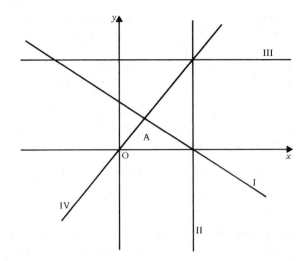

The graph shows four straight lines, labelled I, II, III and IV, whose equations are $x = 2$, $y = 4$, $y = 2x$ and $x + y = 2$.

(a) State clearly the equation of each.

(b) Shade the area which satisfies all the inequalities:

$$x > 0, \quad x < 2, \quad y < 4, \quad y > 2x, \quad y > 2 - x$$

(c) Give all the inequalities necessary to define the region A.

Simultaneous Linear Equations   9

Solve the given pairs of simultaneous equations:

1   $x + y = 8$
    $x - y = 2$

2   $2x + y = 5$
    $x - y = 4$

3   $5x + y = 8$
    $x - y = 4$

4   $3x + y = 11$
    $x + y = 3$

5   $x + 3y = 13$
    $x + 2y = 9$

6   $x - 3y = 7$
    $x + y = 3$

7   $2x + y = 7$
    $3x + 2y = 12$

8   $5x - y = 17$
    $2x + 3y = 0$

9   $3x + 2y = 3$
    $2x + 3y = 7$

10   $5x + 7y = 4$
    $x + 2y = 2$

11   $4x - y = 10$
    $3x + 5y = 19$

12   $3x + 5y = -14$
    $3x - 2y = 14$

13   $7x + 5y = 6$
    $3x - 4y = 21$

14   $5x - 3y = 11$
    $4x + y = 19$

15    $8x - y = 6$
      $7x + 5y = 17$

16    $3x + 4y = 26$
      $4x - 3y = 18$

17    $5x + y = 22$
      $2x - 5y = 25$

18    $3x - 4y = 30$
      $4x + 5y = 9$

19   A year ago a mother was four times as old as her daughter. In three years time she will be three times as old as her daughter. Find the present age of the daughter.

20   A year ago a father was four times as old as his son. Three years ago he was five times as old as his son. Find his son's age in two years time.

21   Five apples and three oranges cost £1.35 whereas three apples and five oranges cost £1.45. Find the cost of an orange and the cost of an apple.

22   Two pens and five pencils cost £1.20 whereas three pens and two pencils cost £1.14. Find the cost of each.

23   The cost of printing 5 large photographs and 12 small photographs is £6.64, while the cost of printing 7 large and 10 small is £7.12. Find the cost of one large and one small.

24   A bookseller offers the same book either with a hard cover or with a soft cover. Three copies of the hard cover together with ten copies of the soft cover cost £26.80, whereas five copies of the hard cover and twenty-one copies of the soft cover cost £52.25. Find the cost of each type of book.

25   Two numbers are such that if 11 is added to the first the answer is twice the second, and if 25 is subtracted from the first the answer is half the second. Find the two numbers.

26   Two motorists arrive at a petrol station. The first buys 5 gallons of petrol and 2 pints of oil and pays £11.70. The second buys 8 gallons of petrol and 3 pints of oil and pays £18.60. Find the price of petrol per gallon and oil per pint.

27   In a supermarket 3 jars of lime marmalade together with 5 jars of orange marmalade cost £4.30, while 5 jars of lime and 4 jars of orange cost £5. Find the cost per jar of each type of marmalade.

28   Alison buys 4 jars of coffee and 3 packets of tea for £9.40 while Bernard buys 5 jars of coffee and 6 packets of tea for £13.55. If Caroline buys one jar of each how much will she have to pay?

29   It cost Mr and Mrs Davis and their two children £16 to go into the motor show, while it cost Mr Easton and his four children £17. Find the cost of entry for one adult and one child.

30 Mr and Mrs Smith and their three children went with Mrs Jones and her two children to the pantomime. The cost for the Smith family was £20.75 while Mrs Jones paid £11.80. Find the price of a ticket for an adult and the price of a ticket for a child. How much would it cost a party of five adults and six children to go to the pantomime?

Algebraic Factors

10

Factorise:

1 $x^2 + 4x$ 2 $x^2 - 8x$

3 $8a^2 - 2a$ 4 $9b^2 + 27b$

5 $x^2 + 7x + 12$ 6 $x^2 + 6x + 5$

7 $x^2 + 9x + 14$ 8 $x^2 + 7x + 10$

9 $a^2 + 11a + 28$ 10 $6 + 5b + b^2$

11 $m^2 + 13m + 42$ 12 $n^2 + 12n + 27$

13 $x^2 + x - 12$ 14 $x^2 + 2x - 15$

15 $x^2 + 5x - 14$ 16 $20 - a - a^2$

17 $b^2 - 3b - 28$ 18 $12 + 4m - m^2$

19 $t^2 - 7t - 18$ 20 $x^2 - 8x + 15$

21 $x^2 - 9x + 14$ 22 $30 - 11x + x^2$

23 $a^2 - 9a + 20$ 24 $b^2 - 3b + 2$

25 $c^2 - 15c + 56$ 26 $y^2 - 11y + 28$

27 $2x^2 + 5x + 2$ 28 $3x^2 + 10x + 3$

29 $5x^2 + 27x + 10$ 30 $3b^2 + 13b + 14$

31 $4a^2 + 23a + 15$ 32 $5a^2 + 21a + 4$

33 $2x^2 - 3x - 2$ 34 $3x^2 - 13x - 10$

35 $5x^2 - 14x - 3$ 36 $5a^2 - 6a - 8$

37 $6 + 19a - 7a^2$ 38 $6x^2 + 11x + 4$

39 $10x^2 + 19x + 6$ 40 $28x^2 + 15x + 2$

41 $15a^2 + 22a + 8$ 42 $14b^2 + 19b + 6$

43 $6x^2 - 5x - 4$ 44 $10x^2 - 11x - 6$

45 $x^2 - 9$ 46 $x^2 - 25$

47 $4x^2 - 25$ 48 $9x^2 - 16$

49    $ab + a + b + 1$ 50 $2mn + 4m + 3n + 6$

51    $2cd + 2c - 2d - 2$ 52 $2mn + 4n - m - 2$

53    $20 - 3y - 2y^2$ 54 $8 + 10x - 12x^2$

55    $ax - bx + ay - by$ 56 $ax - 2ay + 2by - bx$

57    $3xy - 2y + 9x - 6$ 58 $ac + bc + 2a + 2b$

59    $mn + 2n - m - 2$ 60 $ab - 2b + 3a - 6$

Quadratic Equations 1   **11**

Solve the following equations:

1    $(x - 3)(x - 5) = 0$ 2 $(x - 7)(x - 4) = 0$

3    $(x + 4)(x - 2) = 0$ 4 $(x - 5)(x + 2) = 0$

5    $(x + 3)(x + 4) = 0$ 6 $(x + 5)(x + 8) = 0$

7    $(2x - 1)(x - 3) = 0$ 8 $(3x - 2)(x - 7) = 0$

9    $(3x - 2)(2x - 5) = 0$ 10 $(4x - 7)(3x - 2) = 0$

11    $(4x + 1)(x - 3) = 0$ 12 $(3x + 2)(x - 5) = 0$

13    $(7x + 3)(5x + 2) = 0$ 14 $(4x + 5)(3x + 10) = 0$

15    $x(x + 5) = 0$ 16 $x(x - 7) = 0$

17    $(x + 2)(x - 2) = 0$ 18 $(x - 5)(x + 5) = 0$

19    $x^2 - 7x = 0$ 20 $x^2 + 9x = 0$

21    $x^2 - 25 = 0$ 22 $x^2 - 16 = 0$

23    $x^2 - 14x + 13 = 0$ 24 $x^2 - 13x + 12 = 0$

25    $x^2 + 6x + 8 = 0$ 26 $x^2 + 7x + 12 = 0$

27    $3x^2 - 4x = 0$ 28 $5x^2 + 6x = 0$

29    $x^2 + 10x + 25 = 0$ 30 $x^2 - 18x + 81 = 0$

31    $3x^2 - 13x + 4 = 0$ 32 $7x^2 + 13x - 2 = 0$

33    $8x^2 + 10x - 3 = 0$ 34 $5x^2 - 19x - 4 = 0$

35    $2x^2 + 5x = 3$ 36 $20 = 9x - x^2$

37    $2x^2 - 4x = 6$ 38 $3x^2 - 18x + 27 = 0$

39    $x^2 + 8 = 6x$ 40 $x^2 + 12 = 8x$

41 Two positive whole numbers differ by 7 and their product is 60. Find them.

42 The length of a lawn is 4 metres more than its width. If the area of the lawn is 96 square metres find its width.

43 In a right-angled triangle the longest side is 6 cm more than the shortest side, and the third side is the average of the other two. Find the three sides.

44 The side of one square is 5 cm longer than the side of another square. Find the sum of their areas, given that the difference in their areas is 95 cm².

45 A rectangular lawn, measuring 30 metres by 18 metres, is surrounded by a path of uniform width. If the total area of the path is 100 square metres, find its width.

46 David is x years old. If his father's age is three years less than the square of David's age, and the sum of their ages is 53 years, form an equation in x and solve it. How old is David's father?

47 Find the price of grapefruit if, when the price rises by 8 p each, I can buy two fewer for £1.92.

48 The average speed of a train travelling the 96 miles from Leicester to London is 16 miles per hour faster than a car making the same journey. The journey by car takes $\frac{1}{2}$ hour longer than the journey by train. Copy and complete the table in terms of v.

	Average speed (in m.p.h.)	Time (in hours)	Distance (in miles)
Car	v	$\dfrac{96}{v}$	96
Train			

Hence form an equation in v and solve it to find:
(a) the average speed of the car,   (b) the time taken by the train.

49 Mr and Mrs Hollins and their son Philip wish to visit Philip's grandparents who live in Bilstone, which is 24 miles away by road from their home. Philip does not like travelling by car so sets out on his bicycle and takes a route that is 4 miles shorter than the most direct

31

route by car. Mr and Mrs Hollins leave home 40 minutes after Philip and are able to travel at an average speed that is 21 m.p.h. faster than Philip is able to cycle. All three arrive at their destination together.

Copy and complete the following table.

	Average speed (in m.p.h.)	Time (in hours)	Distance (in miles)
Bicycle	v	$\dfrac{20}{v}$	20
Car	$v + 21$		24

Hence form an equation in v and solve it.

(a) What was Philip's average speed on his bicycle?

(b) How long did Mr and Mrs Hollins take to complete the journey?

50 A commercial traveller sets out from Nottingham to drive the 140 kilometres to Chester. After completing her journey she realises that had she increased her average speed of x km/h by 10 km/h she would have arrived 20 minutes earlier. Copy and complete the following table.

	Speed (in km/h)	Time (in hours)	Distance (in km)
At the slower speed	x	$\dfrac{140}{x}$	140
At the faster speed	$x + 10$		

Form an equation in x and solve it. At what average speed did she actually make the journey? How long did she take?

Quadratic Equations 2   12

In the following examples whenever the square roots will not evaluate exactly give them correct to two decimal places.

Solve:

1 $(x - 1)^2 = 100$

2 $(x - 2)^2 = 10$

3 $(x - 3)^2 = 20$

4 $(x - 4)^2 = 55$

5 $(x - 5)^2 = 83$

6 $(x + 2)^2 = 6$

7 $(x + 3)^2 = 18$

8 $(x + 4)^2 = 36$

9 $(x + 1)^2 = 19$

10 $(x - 2.5)^2 = 28.6$

Complete the square for each of the following expressions:

11    $x^2 + 6x$ 12 $x^2 + 8x$

13    $x^2 + 12x$ 14 $x^2 - 10x$

15    $x^2 - 20x$ 16 $x^2 - 8x$

17    $x^2 + 3x$ 18 $x^2 + 5x$

19    $x^2 - 7x$ 20 $x^2 - 13x$

21    $x^2 + \frac{3}{2}x$ 22 $x^2 + \frac{5}{4}x$

23    $x^2 + \frac{6}{7}x$ 24 $x^2 - \frac{4}{5}x$

25    $x^2 - \frac{12}{7}x$ 26 $4x^2 + 4x$

Solve each of the following equations either by completing the square or by using the formula. Give all answers correct to two decimal places.

27    $x^2 + 4x + 2 = 0$ 28 $x^2 + 5x + 3 = 0$

29    $x^2 + 5x + 6 = 0$ 30 $x^2 + 5x + 5 = 0$

31    $x^2 + 6x + 7 = 0$ 32 $x^2 - 5x - 7 = 0$

33    $x^2 - 5x + 3 = 0$ 34 $x^2 - 6x + 6 = 0$

35    $x^2 - 7x + 9 = 0$ 36 $x^2 - 7x + 10 = 0$

37    $x^2 + 4x - 7 = 0$ 38 $x^2 - 5x + 2 = 0$

39    $x^2 - 8x + 3 = 0$ 40 $x^2 + 5x + 3 = 0$

41    $x^2 + 9x - 2 = 0$ 42 $x^2 - 4x - 7 = 0$

43    $x^2 + 12x - 3 = 0$ 44 $x^2 - 7x + 2 = 0$

45    $x^2 - 6x + 6 = 0$ 46 $x^2 + 5x - 4 = 0$

47    $2x^2 + 3x - 4 = 0$ 48 $2x^2 - 4x - 5 = 0$

49    $3x^2 + 9x + 4 = 0$ 50 $5x^2 + 3x - 5 = 0$

51    $8x^2 + 10x + 1 = 0$ 52 $7x^2 - 12x + 3 = 0$

53    $4x^2 + 8x + 1 = 0$ 54 $10x^2 - 3x - 2 = 0$

55    $8x^2 + 9x - 7 = 0$ 56 $4x^2 - x - 4 = 0$

57    $7x^2 + 10x + 1 = 0$ 58 $\dfrac{x^2}{2} + 3x + 1 = 0$

59    $\dfrac{x^2}{2} + 5x + 3 = 0$ 60 $\dfrac{x^2}{2} - 5x + 4 = 0$

61    $\dfrac{x^2}{3} + 4x + 7 = 0$ 62 $3x + 4 = \dfrac{1}{x}$

63    $5x - 7 = \dfrac{2}{x}$ 64 $\dfrac{3}{x} + 12 + 7x = 0$

65    $\dfrac{3}{x} - x - 4 = 0$ 66 $\dfrac{1}{x} - 4x + 2 = 0$

67    $0.7x^2 + 4.2x + 0.4 = 0$ 68 $1.4x^2 + 3.9x + 2.3 = 0$

69    $2.3x^2 + 0.9x - 1.2 = 0$ 70 $5.7x^2 + 2.7x - 3.9 = 0$

71    $3.4x^2 - 5.2x - 1.9 = 0$ 72 $2(2x^2 - 1) = 5x$

73    $5(x - 1) = x^2 - 3$ 74 $4x(x - 1) = 9$

75    $10x(2 - x) = 7$ 76 $\dfrac{1}{x + 1} + \dfrac{1}{x} = 4$

77    $\dfrac{2}{2x - 1} + \dfrac{3}{x} = 6$ 78 $\dfrac{x - 3}{x - 2} = \dfrac{3x + 2}{x - 4}$

79    $\dfrac{2x - 1}{x + 7} = \dfrac{x + 2}{3x + 4}$ 80 $\dfrac{1}{3x - 1} = 1 - \dfrac{3x - 2}{5}$

In the following questions, give any answers which do not work out exactly correct to two decimal places.

81   In a trapezium the parallel sides are of length x cm and $x + 2$ cm. If the distance between these parallel sides is $\frac{1}{2}x$ cm and the area of the trapezium is 15 cm², form an equation in x and solve it to find the dimensions of the figure.

82   The sum of the first n natural numbers is $\dfrac{n(n + 1)}{2}$. Find n if the sum of the first n numbers is 300.

83   The sum of the squares of three consecutive positive whole numbers is 302. Find them.

84   One side of a rectangle is two metres longer than the other. If the length of a diagonal is eight metres, find the sides.

85   One side of a rectangle is 5 m shorter than the other. If the length of a diagonal is 14 m find the sides.

86   The hypotenuse of a right-angled triangle is 19 cm and the sum of the lengths of the other two sides is 24 cm. Find these sides.

87   A picture measuring 30 cm by 20 cm is surrounded by a frame whose area is 216 cm². Find the width of the frame.

88   The area of the page of a book is 216 cm². If the length is half as long again as the width, find the dimensions of the page.

89   The area of the page of a book is 300 cm². If the length is 5 cm more than the width, find the dimensions of the page.

90 A straight-sided plane figure with n sides has $\dfrac{n(n-3)}{2}$ diagonals. If such a figure has 54 diagonals how many sides does it have?

91 A building-site foreman has 20 metres of fencing with which to erect three sides of a rectangular pen, the fourth side being an existing wall. If the area of the pen is 40 m² find its dimensions.

92 A rectangular lawn measuring 10 metres by 8 metres is surrounded by a path of uniform width x metres. If the area of the path is 60 m² find x.

93 A stone thrown vertically into the air is h metres above the ground after t seconds where $h = 30t - 5t^2$. When is the stone 40 metres above the ground? Explain the two answers.

94 A wooden block is x cm long, $\frac{1}{2}x$ cm wide and $\frac{1}{3}x$ cm high. If the total surface area of the block is 72 cm² find x.

95 A circular lawn of radius r metres is surrounded by a uniform path one metre wide. If the area of the path is one-tenth the area of the lawn, find the radius of the lawn.

Similar Shapes   13

1 Fill in the blanks in the following table which gives information for similar figures. (Some of the ratios are not in their simplest form.)

Ratio of lengths	Ratios of areas
2:3	4:9
2:1	
5:2	
3:4	
1:x	
$x:y$	
$3x:5x$	
	100:81
	50:32
	28:63
	$9y^2:1$
	$16z^2:25y^2$

35

2 Fill in the blanks in the following table which gives information for similar solids. (Some of the ratios are not in their simplest form.)

Ratio of lengths	Ratio of volumes
3:2	27:8
1:2	
2:3	
5:4	
7:4	
$x:y$	
$4x:3y$	
	1000:64
	$x^3:8y^3$
	8:1
	54:16
	7000:189

3 How do you convert:
(a) cm into m
(b) m^2 into cm^2
(c) m into km
(d) m^3 into cm^3
(e) mm into cm
(f) cm^2 into mm^2?

4 An Ordnance Survey map has a map ratio of 1:50 000. Find the real-life values which correspond to the following details from the map.
(a) two towns 20 cm apart,
(b) a wood of area 5 cm^2,
(c) a river 0.8 cm wide,
(d) a lake of area 2.8 cm^2.

5 An Ordnance Survey map has a map ratio of 1:25 000. Find the corresponding distances/areas on the map for:
(a) two villages 4 kilometres apart,
(b) a reservoir of area 1.2 km^2,
(c) a churchyard of area 2500 m^2,
(d) a street $\frac{1}{2}$ km long.

6 A map of Europe has a map ratio of 1:2 000 000. Find:
(a) the distance, in kilometres, between two places which are 10 cm apart on the map,
(b) the length, on the map in cm, of a river which is 80 km long.

7 Assuming that an orange is a sphere of diameter 9 cm and that the peel is uniformly 9 mm thick, find the percentage remaining when it has been peeled.

8 Comparing two action-man sets, the surface areas of two similar waistcoats worn by the two 'men' are 50 cm² and 72 cm². If the smaller 'man' is 26 cm tall and the larger 'man' has a volume of 360 cm³ find:

(a) the volume of the smaller 'man',

(b) the height of the larger 'man'.

9 A nursery offers six different sizes of flower pots, viz. 5 cm, 8 cm, 10 cm, 15 cm, 20 cm and 25 cm. If one bag of John Innes potting compost will fill ten 10 cm pots how many bags are required to fill ten of each of the six sizes?

10 Three similar apples from the same tree have surface areas of 50 cm², 72 cm² and 162 cm². If the volume of the largest apple is 364 cm³ and its girth is 27 cm find:

(a) the girth of the smallest,

(b) the volume of the middle-sized apple.

11 Two houses A and B are identical in design but different in size, the floor area of B being 21% greater than that of A.

In house A the ceilings are 2.4 m high, the volume of the main bedroom is 30 m³, and the area of the lounge carpet is 17.5 m². Calculate the corresponding values for house B.

In house B, the third bedroom has a volume of 14.641 m³, the area of its window is 4.598 m² and the depth of the skirting board is 7.7 cm. Calculate the corresponding values for house A.

12 It is found that a model aeroplane will fly if its weight to wing surface area is in a ratio less than 1:2. A model aeroplane which is 15 cm long has a wing area of 100 cm² and weighs 20 g. Which of the following model aeroplanes, made from similar materials, can be expected to fly?

Aeroplane	Length
A	20 cm
B	30 cm
C	45 cm
D	50 cm

13 A motor-vehicle manufacturer produces a range of three similar cars with engine capacities 1000 cc, 1728 cc and 2197 cc. If the largest car is 468 cm long, has a fuel tank of capacity 14 gallons, a windscreen of area 1.014 m² and is 169 cm wide find the corresponding values for the other two cars.

14 Three cups belonging to a set have similar shapes. The breakfast cup is 7 cm high, the tea cup 6 cm high and the coffee cup is 5 cm high. If the tea cup holds 216 cm³ find the volume of:

(a) the coffee cup,   (b) the breakfast cup.

15 Three similar jugs have volumes 343 cm³, 729 cm³ and 1331 cm³. If the middle jug is 9 cm tall find:

(a) the height of the smallest jug,

(b) the height of the largest jug,

(c) the ratio of the surface areas of liquid visible in the three jugs.

16 A chocolate biscuit is in the form of a circular disc 8 cm in diameter and 12 mm thick. It is coated on one side with chocolate one milli-metre thick. The manufacturer decides to introduce a new biscuit 7 cm in diameter and proportionately thinner, but to leave the thickness of the chocolate coating unchanged. Find:

(a) the percentage saving in biscuit materials,

(b) the percentage saving in chocolate.

Give your answers correct to the nearest whole number.

Nets

1

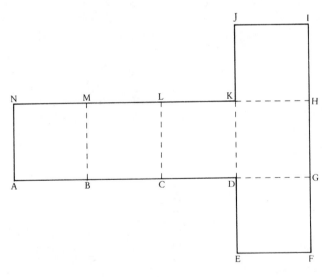

The diagram shows a net for a cube.

(a) Which point meets with N?

(b) Which line meets with EF?

(c) If the cube is placed with square DGHK on the table, which square is on the top?

(d) If the cube is placed with DGFE on the table, which square is on the top?

(e) Copy the sketch of the cube and place each of the letters given above in the correct position on the sketch. E, C at the same vertex indicates that these two points come together.

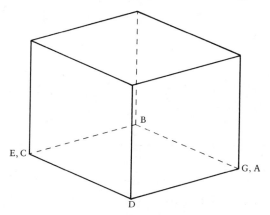

(f) Draw a different net for the same cube. Do not put letters on it.

2

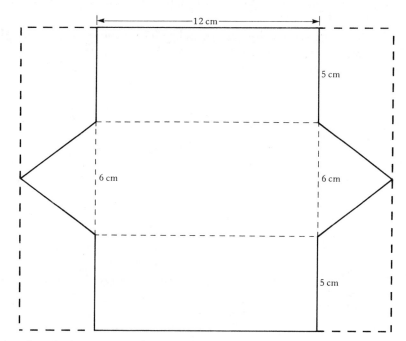

The sketch shows a net for a prism. Find:

(a) the area of one of the triangular faces,

(b) the total surface area of the prism,

(c) the volume of the prism.

State the dimensions of the smallest rectangular sheet of card from which the given net may be cut.

3

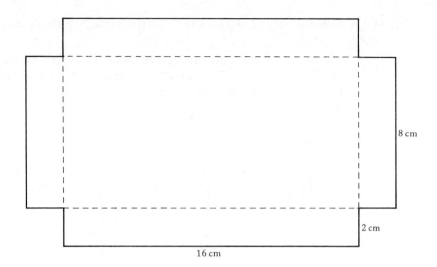

This net can be folded to make an open box. Find:

(a) the capacity of the box,

(b) the total external area of the box,

(c) the length of the longest straight line that can be drawn on the base of the box,

(d) the length of the longest straight piece of wire that can be placed completely within the box.

4

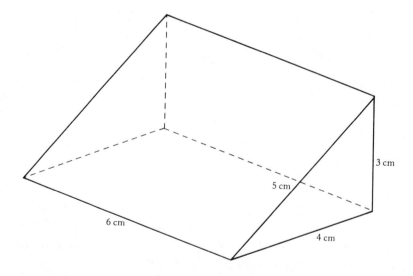

Study this triangular prism.

(a) Draw a net for it which has one axis of symmetry.

(b) Draw a net for it which does not have an axis of symmetry.

(c) Draw the net for this triangular prism so that it may be cut from the smallest possible piece of rectangular card.

5

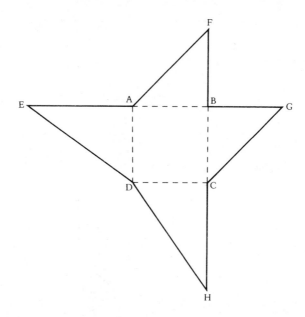

The diagram gives the net of a pyramid with a square base. When the pyramid is formed:

(a) Which letters coincide with E?

(b) What special position does E have with respect to the corners of the base ABCD?

6   VABCD is a pyramid with a square base ABCD of side 4 cm. The perpendicular distance from V to each of the sides of the square is 6 cm. Draw an accurate net that could be used to make this pyramid. Find the area of this net. What is the length of the side of the smallest square of card from which this pyramid could be cut? How many axes of symmetry has the net with the square in the centre?

7   Which of the sketches given below are nets for a cube?

(a)   (b)

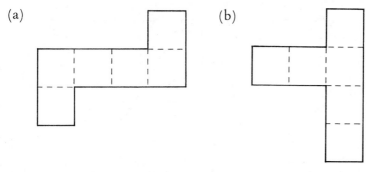

(continued overleaf)

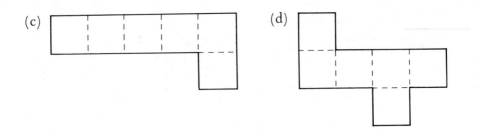

(c)   (d)

8   Which of the sketches given below are nets for a square-based pyramid?

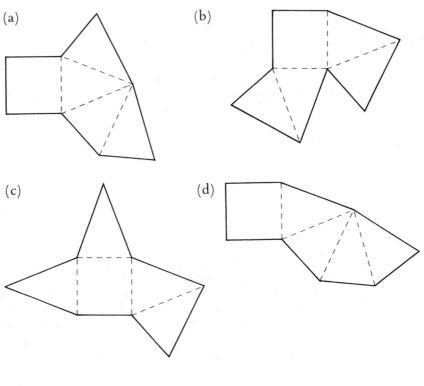

(a)   (b)

(c)   (d)

9

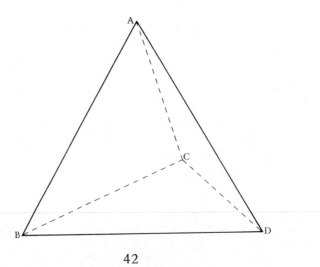

ABCD is a regular tetrahedron with an edge of length 5 cm.

(a) Draw a net for this solid and letter it so that the faces BAD and ACD are adjacent.

(b) Use this net to find the shortest distance from the midpoint of BD, over the edge AD, to the midpoint of CD.

10 What solid can be made from this net?

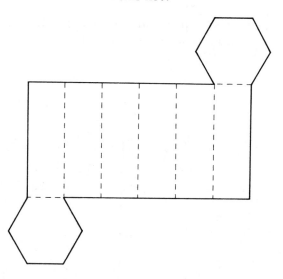

11 The following net has one face missing.

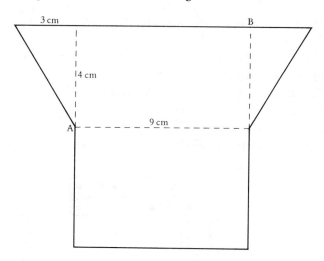

(a) Copy the net and add the missing face in one of its possible positions. In how many different positions could the missing face be drawn? Fill in missing measurements.

(b) Name the solid formed by the net and sketch it.

(c) Find:
    (i) the total surface area of the solid,
    (ii) the volume of the solid.

(d) Find the distance AB:
    (i) on the net you have drawn,
    (ii) by calculation.

12   ABCD is the base of a pyramid with a square base of side 5 cm. The vertex E is vertically above the point of intersection, F, of AC and BD, and AE = 5 cm.

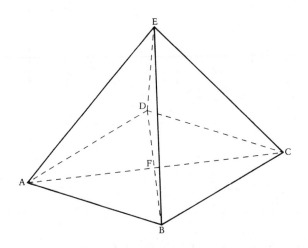

(a) Draw an accurate net for this pyramid and use it to find the distance AC.

(b) Draw triangle AEC accurately and hence find the height of the pyramid EF.

(c) Calculate the volume of the pyramid.

13

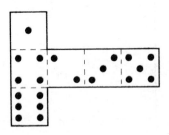

The sketch shows the net for a cube which can be used as a die. All the dots on it are in their correct positions and directions.

(a) Given below are three other nets for a cube. Copy each of them and draw in the correct positions and directions for the dots.

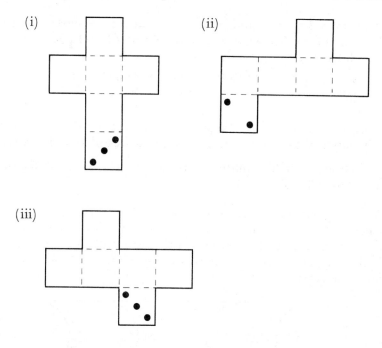

(i)

(ii)

(iii)

(b) Show the position of the dots and their directions for each of the cubes given below. Include what appears on the hidden faces from directions A, B and C.

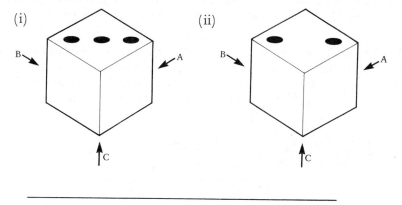

(i)

(ii)

Area and Volume

15

1   A room is 2 m wide and 3.6 m long and is to be covered with carpet from a roll 90 cm wide which is sold at £12.60 per running metre length from the roll. Find:

(a) the total length of carpet required from the roll,

(b) its cost.

2   The area of a leaf (both sides) on a tree is 35 cm². If there are 556 000 leaves on the tree, find the total area of all the leaves in m².

If each leaf is half a millimetre thick, find the total volume of all the leaves in m³.

3   A rectangular lawn measures 40 m by 25 m. A man mows it along its length using a machine which cuts to a width of 50 cm. Neglecting the turn at each end, how far will the man walk in mowing the lawn? If the mower travels at 2 metres per second, how long will it take to mow the lawn?

4

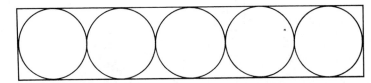

Five circular pieces of metal each of radius 22 cm are cut from a rectangular sheet of metal measuring 220 cm by 44 cm. Find the area of metal wasted and express this as a percentage of the whole sheet. Give each answer correct to the nearest whole number.

5   The walls of a bathroom are to be tiled to halfway using square tiles measuring 6 in by 6 in sold in boxes containing 25 tiles (only full boxes are sold) and priced £6.75 per box. If the room is 72 in long, 60 in wide and 96 in high, and the untiled door is 30 in wide, calculate:

(a) the number of tiles required,

(b) the number of boxes required,

(c) the total cost.

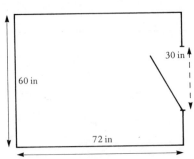

6

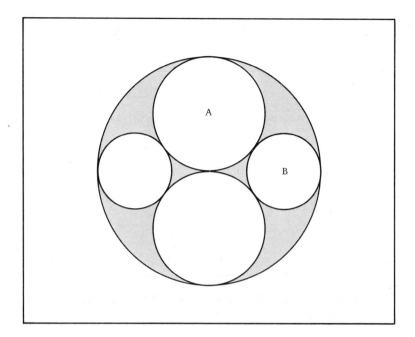

The diagram shows the design for a new flag for the country of Ruritania. It consists of a circle, radius 30 cm, set in a rectangle measuring 100 cm by 80 cm. Within this circle are four smaller circles, as shown in the diagram. The flag is symmetrical about the horizontal and vertical axes through its centre.

(a) Write down the radius of circle A.

(b) Find the radius of circle B.

(c) Calculate, in terms of π, the total area that is shaded.

(d) Find the sum, in terms of π, of the perimeters of the shapes which make up the shaded areas.

7 Thirty cubes, each with edges of length 1 cm, are fixed together to form a solid rectangular block.

(a) If the perimeter of the base is 14 cm, find its height.

(b) If the block is 2 cm high, find the perimeter of its base.

8 Rectangular boxes of biscuits measure 12.5 cm × 8 cm × 4 cm. Eighteen such boxes are packed in three layers in what is called an 'outer'.

(a) If the base of an outer measures 25 cm × 24 cm draw a sketch to show how the boxes are placed in the outer. How many boxes are there in each layer?

(b) Find the volume of an outer in cm³.

(c) The floor of a lorry measures 5 m × 2.4 m and it is 3 m high. How many outers can the lorry carry?

9

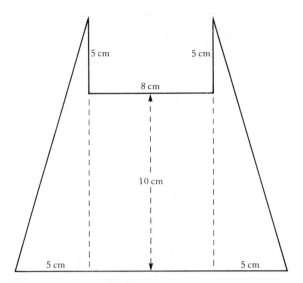

The diagram shows the cross-section of a metal casting that is one metre long. Find:

(a) the area of the cross-section in square centimetres,

(b) the area of the sloping faces in square centimetres,

(c) the volume of the casting in (i) cm^3 (ii) m^3,

(d) the mass of the casting, in kilograms, if each cubic centimetre has a mass of 8 grams.

10 A swimming pool is 50 m long and 20 m wide. The depth varies uniformly from 1 metre at the shallow end to 2.5 metres at the deep end. Calculate the volume of water in the pool when:

(a) it is full,

(b) half the surface area of the bottom is visible.

11

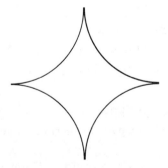

The sketch shows the plan for a flowerbed. It is formed from four quarter circles, each of radius 4 metres. Use the value of π on your calculator to find:

(a) the perimeter of the flower bed,

(b) its area.

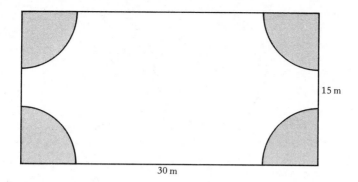

12

30 m

15 m

The diagram shows a rectangular garden, measuring 30 m by 15 m. It has flowerbeds at the corners, each in the form of a quarter of a circle of radius 5 m. The remainder of the garden is lawn. Taking $\pi = 3$ find:

(a) the combined area of the four flowerbeds,

(b) the area of the lawn,

(c) the perimeter of the lawn.

13 Each portion in a circular pack of six cheeses is 1.2 cm thick. The radius of the pack is 4.3 cm, and each portion is covered completely on the top by a label. Find:

(a) the perimeter and area of a label,

(b) the volume of cheese in one portion.

14 (a) Calculate the volume of an orange squash tank which is in the shape of a circular cylinder with base radius 21 cm and height 30 cm (take $\pi = \frac{22}{7}$).

(b) How many litres of squash does a tank hold? (Give your answer correct to three significant figures.)

(c) At the beginning of the day the cafe owner fills the tank to the 40 litre mark, and at the end of the day he finds it has fallen to the 12 litre mark. The squash costs him 50 p a litre and he sells it at 24 p per quarter litre glass. If three glasses of squash have been wasted, find:

　(i) the number of glasses sold,

　(ii) the cash received from their sale,

　(iii) the profit for the day.

15 A cylindrical can of cleansing powder has a radius 4 cm and height 20 cm. Twenty-five such cans are packed into a carton 40 cm X 40 cm X 20 cm. Calculate the amount of waste space in the carton giving your answer correct to three significant figures.

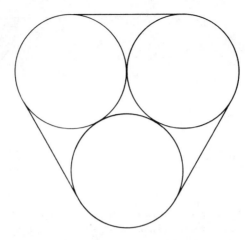

16

Three pieces of wooden dowel, each of diameter 2 cm, are held together by a stretched elastic band as shown in the diagram.

(a) If the stretched length of the elastic band is twice its unstretched length calculate:
    (i) the stretched length,
    (ii) the unstretched length of the band.

(b) If a fourth piece of similar dowel is pushed in with the others so that they all take up positions as shown in the second diagram, how much additional stretching of the elastic band will be required?

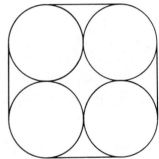

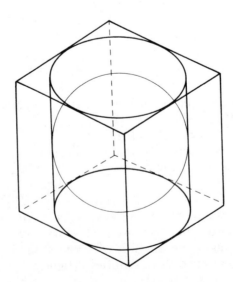

17

A sphere just fits inside a cylinder, which in turn just fits inside a cube of side 10 cm. Find:

(a) the volume of the space between the cylinder and the cube,

(b) the volume of the space between the cylinder and the sphere.

Express your answer to (a) as a percentage of your answer to (b).

18 Twelve golf balls are sold in a rectangular box whose depth is equal to the diameter of a ball. The dimensions of the box are such that the golf balls cannot move about. What percentage of the space within the box is unfilled? Give your answer correct to the nearest whole number.

19 Three tennis balls are sold in a cylindrical container. The internal diameter of the container is equal to the diameter of a tennis ball, and the height of the container is such that the tennis balls cannot move about. What fraction of the space within the container is occupied by the tennis balls?

20

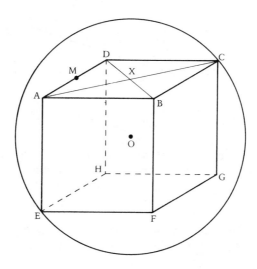

The diagram shows the largest cube that can be cut from a solid sphere, centre O, radius 9 cm. All the vertices A, B, C, D, E, F, G and H lie in the surface of the sphere.

Let M be the midpoint of AD, X the intersection of the diagonals AC and BD, and let the side of the cube be of length 2*a* cm.

(a) Find in terms of *a*, the length of:
    (i) AM   (ii) MX   (iii) AX   (iv) XO   (v) AO

(b) Use the fact that OA is the radius of the original sphere to find, correct to three significant figures, the length of a side of the cube.

21 A closed rectangular water tank is 2 m long, 1.5 m wide and 1 m deep. Find:

(a) the total surface area of the tank,

(b) the amount of water it holds when half full, giving your answer in cubic metres.

22 Wine from a full cylindrical bottle of 7 cm diameter and height 16 cm is poured into glasses in the form of a hemisphere of radius $2\frac{1}{2}$ cm. How many glasses may be completely filled?

23 The volume of a cube is 100 cm³. Find the length of an edge and the area of a face, giving each answer correct to three significant figures.

24 Find the volume of a circular biscuit 7 cm in diameter and 5 mm thick. Give your answer in cm³ (take $\pi = \frac{22}{7}$).

25 Perfume is bought at £124.60 per litre and is sold in 12.5 ml bottles at £2.30 per bottle. Find the total profit.

26

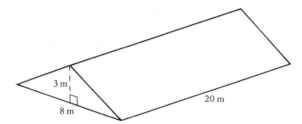

The diagram shows a roof which covers a building 20 m long and 8 m wide. If the cross-section of the roof is 3 m high, find:

(a) the length of a sloping side of the roof,

(b) the total area of the two sloping sides of the roof,

(c) the volume of rain which will fall on the roof during a storm when 2 cm of rain falls vertically. Give your answer in m³.

27 A sphere of ice-cream 6 cm in diameter melts and flows into a cone whose depth is equal to three times its radius. If the melted ice-cream fills the cone completely and it is assumed that there is no change in volume, find the depth of the cone giving your answer correct to one decimal place.

28 A rectangular concrete block is 50 cm long, 25 cm high and $12\frac{1}{2}$ cm thick. How many such blocks will be required to build a wall 48 m long, 3 m high and $12\frac{1}{2}$ cm thick? Find the volume of concrete used in m³.

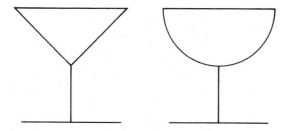

29   One wine glass is in the form of a right circular cone with base radius 4 cm and depth 4 cm and a second wine glass is in the form of a hemisphere of radius 4 cm. If 20 of the conical wine glasses can be filled from a single bottle of wine how many hemispherical glasses may be filled from the same bottle?

30   If water increases in volume by 4% when it freezes, how many cubes of ice of side 2 cm may be obtained from 10 litres of water?

31   The external dimensions of a closed rectangular box, made from wood 5 mm thick, are 10 cm × 9 cm × 8 cm. Calculate:

(a) the total external surface area,

(b) the capacity of the box,

(c) the volume of wood used to make the box.

32   A cylindrical teapot has a diameter of 12 cm and is 15 cm high. How many full hemispherical cups of diameter 9 cm may be poured from this teapot?

33   A mug is in the shape of the frustum of a cone and is 10 cm deep. The diameters of its top and bottom are respectively 8 cm and 6 cm. Find, in terms of π, the volume of liquid the mug will hold.

Travel Graphs   **16**

1   A soldier is to attempt an assault course which is 535 m long. The course has three sections, A to B which is uphill and 300 m long, B to C which is 160 m along level ground and C to D which is 75 m downhill. The soldier can travel at 2 m/s uphill, 4 m/s on level ground and 5 m/s downhill.

(a) Draw a travel graph to represent his attempt. Take 2 cm to represent 25 s and 2 cm to represent 100 m.

(b) How long does his attempt take?

(c) Find his average speed for the whole of the course.

2

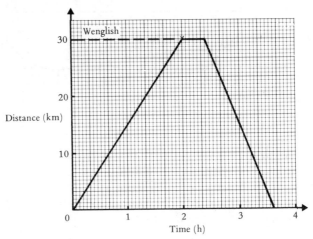

Paula travels from home to Wenglish and back again one afternoon. The travel graph for her journey is given above.

(a) Find her average speed for (i) the outward journey, (ii) the return journey.

(b) How long was she away from home?

(c) Do you think Paula travelled on foot, on a bicycle or in a car? Give a reason for your answer.

3

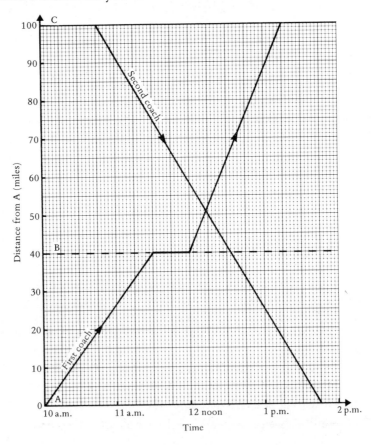

The travel graph opposite shows the journeys of two coaches. The first travels from A to C via B, while the second travels on the same route but in the opposite direction.

From the graph find:

(a) the speed of the first coach (i) between A and B, (ii) between B and C,

(b) the average speed of the first coach for the whole journey,

(c) the average speed of the second coach,

(d) when and where the two coaches pass,

(e) the distance between the coaches at 1 p.m.

4 Antley, Bexeter and Cridgley are three towns (in that order) on a straight road, Antley being 40 miles south of Bexeter and Cridgley 50 miles north of it. A car leaves Antley at noon and travels at a constant speed of 40 m.p.h. to Bexeter where it remains for 20 minutes before travelling on to Cridgley, arriving at 2.40 p.m. A second car leaves Antley at 12.36 p.m. and travels to Cridgley without a stop, arriving at 2.28 p.m.

Using 2 cm ≡ 10 miles and 2 cm ≡ 20 minutes draw suitable travel graphs and use them to find:

(a) when and where they pass,

(b) the speed of the first car for the second part of the journey,

(c) when the second car is exactly 5 miles ahead of the first.

5 A and B are two motorway stops 120 miles apart. One car leaves A at 11.08 a.m. and drives to B, without stopping, at a constant speed, arriving at 1.32 p.m. A second car leaves B for A, travels at a constant 60 m.p.h., and arrives at 1.36 p.m.

Draw travel graphs for these journeys and from them find:

(a) the time of departure from B of the second car,

(b) the average speed of the first car,

(c) when and where they pass,

(d) their distance apart at 1 p.m.

Use 2 cm ≡ 10 miles and 2 cm ≡ 20 minutes.

6 Timothy leaves Doxton at noon to cycle to Longway town 20 miles away. He pedals at a steady speed of 15 m.p.h. but after seventeen miles he has a puncture. After spending 15 min trying to repair his tyre, he decides to push it the rest of the way. This he does at a constant speed of 4 m.p.h. His friend Colin leaves Doxton half an

55

hour after Timothy and travels directly to Longway at a steady speed of 14 m.p.h. Draw travel graphs to illustrate the journeys and use them to find:

(a) the time of arrival of each at Longway,

(b) when and where they pass,

(c) their distance apart one hour after Colin has left Doxton.

Use $6 \, \text{cm} \equiv 5$ miles and $2 \, \text{cm} \equiv 15$ minutes.

7   Two hikers leave a mountain centre A at 8 a.m. and set out on a 12 mile walk to B. They walk at a steady 4 m.p.h. to a check point which is at the halfway stage. After a 15 minute rest they continue at the same speed but two miles from the end of the walk one of them injures his foot and cannot continue. After resting with him for half an hour the second hiker decides to press on to B for help. He walks at 5 m.p.h. At noon the rescue party leaves B and walks towards the injured hiker at a steady 4 m.p.h. The rescue party spends 15 minutes with him, then takes him back to A arriving there at 5 p.m.

Draw a distance–time graph to show these journeys and from it find:

(a) the time the hiker who was seeking help arrived at B,

(b) the time the rescue party reached the injured hiker,

(c) the average speed at which he was transported to A.

Take $3 \, \text{cm} \equiv 2$ miles on the vertical distance axis and $2 \, \text{cm} \equiv 1$ hour on the horizontal time axis.

8   A coaster leaves a port A at noon carrying coal for delivery at three ports B, C and D. It travels to B, a distance of 150 nautical miles, at a steady speed of 12 knots. At B it spends $3\frac{1}{2}$ hours unloading before continuing the journey to C, a further distance of 150 nautical miles. It arrives at C at 9 a.m. the following morning. At C the unloading takes 4 hours. The coaster then proceeds to D, a distance of 200 nautical miles, arriving there at 9 a.m. the following day. A naval protection ship sails from D to A at a steady speed of 25 knots, arriving there at 4 a.m. on the third day.

Draw travel graphs to show these journeys, using $1 \, \text{cm} \equiv 25$ nautical miles on the vertical axis and $2\frac{1}{2}$ hours on the horizontal axis.

Use your graphs to find:

(a) the average speed of the coaster between B and C and between C and D,

(b) the time the protection ship leaves D,

(c) when and where they pass.

9   A motorcycle starts from rest. Its distance, s metres, from the starting
    point after t seconds is given in the table.

t	0	1	2	3	4	5	6
s	0	3	12	27	48	75	108

Draw a distance-time graph using 2 cm to represent 1 second and
2 cm to represent 10 m.

From your graph find:

(a) the distance the motorcycle has travelled after $3\frac{1}{2}$ seconds,

(b) the average speed of the motorcycle in the second second,

(c) the average speed of the motorcycle during the first six seconds,

(d) the speed of the motorcycle when $t = 3\frac{1}{2}$.

10 The velocity–time graph for a particle is given below.

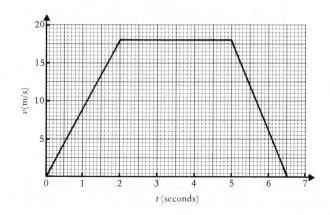

(a) What is the acceleration of the particle?

(b) What is the deceleration of the particle?

(c) For how long does the particle travel at a constant speed?

(d) For how long is the particle decelerating?

(e) How far does the particle travel in (i) the first 3 seconds (ii) the
    whole of its journey?

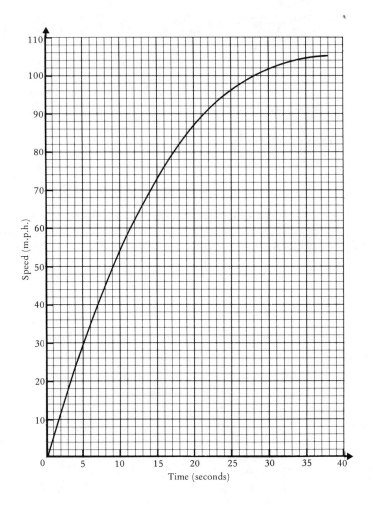

11

The speed of a car on a test drive is observed at regular intervals. The velocity–time graph shown above has been derived from these observations.

(a) Use the graph to estimate:
    (i) its speed after 20 seconds,
    (ii) the time at which its speed is 56 m.p.h.,
    (iii) the highest speed recorded,
    (iv) the time it takes for the speed to increase from 50 m.p.h. to 100 m.p.h.

(b) State briefly how the acceleration of the car changes over the first half minute.

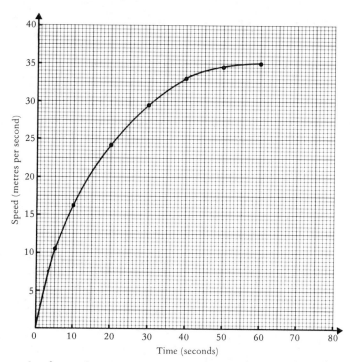

Time (seconds)

The speed of an electric train was observed at various intervals of time and the observations recorded in the following table.

Time (in seconds)	Speed (in m/s)
0	0
5	10.5
10	16.5
20	24.5
30	29.5
40	33
50	34.5
60	35

The velocity-time graph for these observations is shown above. Copy it on to graph paper using 2 cm to represent 10 seconds on the time axis and 2 cm to represent 5 m/s on the speed axis.

(a) Use your graph to estimate:
   (i) the speed after 35 seconds,
   (ii) the acceleration after 20 seconds.

(b) When would the acceleration appear to be greatest?

(c) Use your graph to estimate the distance travelled by the train in the first minute.

(d) The driver applies the brakes 60 seconds after the start of the journey. They produce a constant retardation of 2 m/s². Draw the graph to show this part of the journey. How long after the brakes are applied does it take for the train to stop? How far has it travelled in this time?

13 The table shows the velocity, v m/s, of a car t seconds after it has started to move.

t	0	1	2	3	4	5	6	7
v	0	7	13	18	22	25	27	28

Draw the velocity–time graph, using 2 cm to represent 1 second and 4 cm to represent 5 m/s.

From your graph find:

(a) the velocity after $2\frac{1}{2}$ seconds,

(b) the acceleration after 4 seconds,

(c) the distance covered in the first two seconds,

(d) the distance covered in the third second.

14 The road test for a new motor car recorded speeds at various times after starting as given in the following table.

Time, t (in seconds)	0	4	8	12	16	20	24	28	32	36
Speed, v (in m.p.h.)	0	30	53	70	81	90	97	102	105	107

Taking $2 \text{ cm} \equiv 4$ seconds on the t-axis and $2 \text{ cm} \equiv 10$ m.p.h. on the v-axis plot these data and draw a smooth curve through the points. Use your graph to estimate:

(a) the time which passes before the car reaches 100 m.p.h.,

(b) the speed after 15 seconds.

Circles and Symmetry **17**

In questions 1 to 18 find the angles marked with letters. In each diagram O denotes the centre of the circle.

1

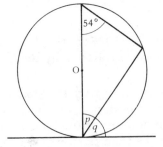

2

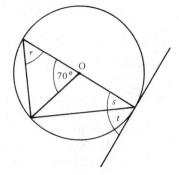

3

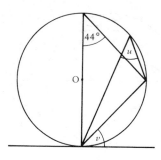

4

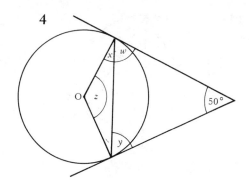

5

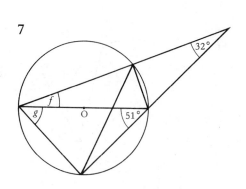

6

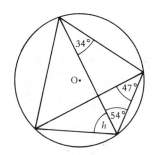

7

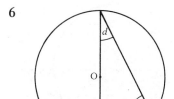

8

9

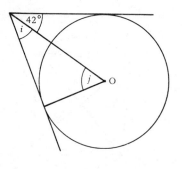

10

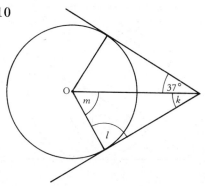

11

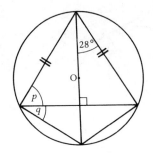

12

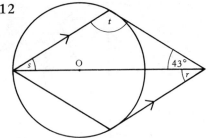

13

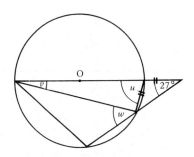

14

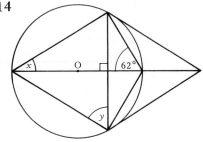

15

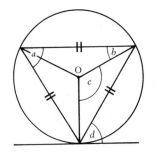

16

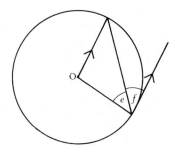

17

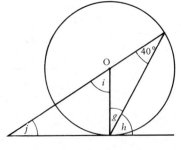

18

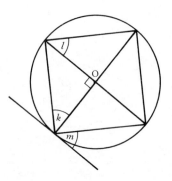

In questions 19 to 23, O is the centre of the circle.

19

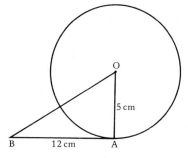

Find: (a) OB   (b) OB̂A

20

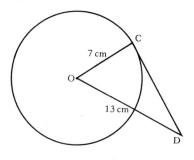

Find: (a) CD   (b) CÔD

21

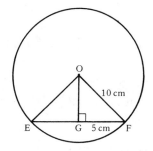

Find: (a) EF   (b) OG
      (c) EÔF

22

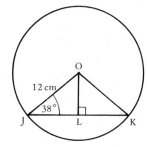

Find: (a) OL   (b) JL
      (c) JK

23

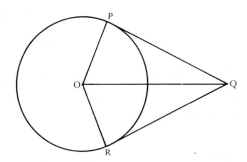

If OQ = 20 cm and PQ̂R = 56° find:
(a) PQ,   (b) the radius of the circle.

24 In the diagram AB, BC and CA are tangents to the circle at P, Q and R respectively. If $\stackrel{\frown}{BAC} = 70°$ and $\stackrel{\frown}{BCA} = 50°$ find:

(a) $\stackrel{\frown}{PRQ}$ (b) $\stackrel{\frown}{BPQ}$ (c) $\stackrel{\frown}{PQR}$

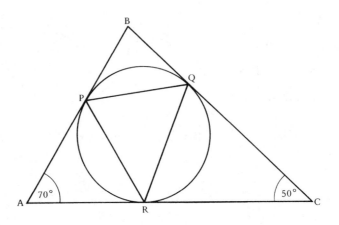

25 AB is a diameter of a circle, centre O, radius 8 cm. C is a point on the circumference such that $\stackrel{\frown}{ABC} = 38°$. Find:

(a) the lengths of the chords AC and BC,

(b) the distance of each of these chords from the centre of the circle.

26 PA and PB are the tangents from P to a circle centre O. If AB = 12 cm and $\stackrel{\frown}{APB} = 56°$ find:

(a) the length of each tangent,

(b) the radius of the circle.

27 The chord AB is 7 cm from the centre, O, of a circle. If $\stackrel{\frown}{AOB} = 104°$ find:

(a) the length of AB,

(b) the radius of the circle.

28 AB is a chord of length 12 cm in a circle, centre O, of radius 8 cm, with AC as the diameter. Find:

(a) the distance of the centre of the circle from the chord AB,

(b) the length of BC,

(c) the distance from the centre of the circle to the chord BC,

(d) the area of triangle ABC.

Constructions

1   Construct a rectangle with adjacent sides of 10.5 cm and 6.8 cm. Measure and record the length of a diagonal.

2   Construct a triangle ABC with AB = 11.5 cm, BC = 9 cm and CA = 7 cm.

3   Construct a triangle PQR in which PQ = 5.5 cm, QR = 6.3 cm and ∠PQR = 120°. Construct the perpendicular from R to PQ produced. Measure and record its length.

4   Construct a triangle XYZ in which XY = 13 cm, YZ = 11 cm and XZ = 7 cm. Construct the circumcircle to this triangle. Measure and record its radius.

5   Construct a rhombus with diagonals of length 7 cm and 5 cm. Measure and record the length of a side of this rhombus.

6   Draw a circle of radius 5 cm and use it to construct a regular hexagon of side 5 cm.

7   Draw a circle of radius 5.5 cm. Construct a regular octagon whose vertices lie on this circle. Measure and record the length of a side of this octagon.

8   Construct a triangle ABC with AB = 9.5 cm, BC = 7 cm and ∠ABC = 30°. By construction find a point D such that ABCD is a parallelogram. Measure and record the lengths of the two diagonals of this parallelogram.

9   Construct a parallelogram ABCD whose diagonals intersect at X given that AC = 10.6 cm, BD = 8.2 cm and ∠AXD = 60°. Measure the lengths of the sides of the parallelogram.

10 Construct a rectangle with diagonals of length 11.2 cm containing an angle of 45°. Measure and record the lengths of the sides of the rectangle.

11 Construct a trapezium ABCD given AB = 12.2 cm, BC = 7.3 cm, DC = 8.5 cm and ∠ABC = 60°. Measure and record the lengths of AD, AC and BD.

12 Construct a triangle PQR in which PR = 8.4 cm, ∠QPR = 30° and ∠QRP = 45°. Construct the circumcircle to this triangle. Measure and record its radius.

13 Draw a circle centre O, radius 6 cm. Construct a regular octagon ABCDEFGH whose vertices lie on this circle. Measure the lengths of:

(a) AB   (b) AD and AF

14 Construct a triangle ABC in which AB = 14 cm, AC = 12 cm and BC = 9 cm. Find a point D on the perpendicular bisector of AB such that the area of triangle ADB is the same as that of ABC. Measure the distance of D from AB and hence estimate the area of triangle ABC.

15 Construct a triangle XYZ in which XY = 12.5 cm, XZ = 10 cm and ZY = 8 cm. Construct the perpendicular bisector of XY and the bisector of angle ZXY. Let these meet in O. With centre O radius OZ describe the arc of a circle which cuts XY at V and W. Measure the length of VW.

16 Construct a triangle ABC with $\angle$ABC = 120°, AB = 6.8 cm and BC = 5.6 cm. Complete the construction of the quadrilateral ABCD where $\angle$ACD = 60° and $\angle$CAD = 45°. Construct the perpendicular from D to AB. Measure and record its length.

Probability   19

1 A letter is chosen at random from the English alphabet. Find the probability that:
   (a) the letter is a vowel,
   (b) the letter is either p or q,
   (c) the letter is one that appears in the word COMPANION.

2 Three unbiased coins are tossed together. What is the probability they show:
   (a) three tails,   (b) two heads and one tail,   (c) no tails?

3 A coin is tossed three times. What is the probability that:
   (a) the first toss gives a head,
   (b) the first two tosses give heads,
   (c) there is at least one head?

4 Two dice are shaken together. What is the probability that:
   (a) the total score is even,
   (b) the total score is a prime number,
   (c) there is at least one six,
   (d) the score on one die is more than the score on the other?

5 The first card drawn from a pack of 52 playing cards is an ace. What is the probability that the second card drawn:
(a) will be an ace,
(b) will not be an ace,
(c) will be a picture card?

6 The first two cards drawn from a pack of 52 playing cards are the King and Queen of hearts. What is the probability that the next card drawn will be:

(a) a heart,   (b) a black card,   (c) a king,
(d) an ace,   (e) a red card,   (f) a black queen?

7 Simon belongs to a class of 30 pupils. Eight of the pupils wear glasses, fourteen are boys and six have blue eyes.
(a) Write down the probability that Simon:
    (i) wears glasses,
    (ii) does not wear glasses,
    (iii) has blue eyes,
    (iv) does not have blue eyes,
    (v) is a boy.
(b) Which one of the above events is:
    (i) most likely,
    (ii) least likely?
(c) What is the probability that if two pupils are chosen at random from the class:
    (i) they are both girls,
    (ii) the first is a boy and the second is a girl?

8 In order to decide the order of play in a badminton competition the names of the six competitors are written on pieces of paper and drawn, one at a time, after being placed in a bag. The competitors are two boys, A and B and four girls, C, D, E and F. Find the probability that:
(a) the first name drawn is B,
(b) the first name drawn is a boy,
(c) the first two names drawn are both boys,
(d) the first two names drawn are both girls.

9 Two dice are tossed. Draw a possibility space to show all the possible outcomes and use it to find the probability that:
(a) a prime number appears on both dice,
(b) the difference between the two numbers shown is 3,
(c) the sum of the two numbers is 8 or more.

10 Three coins are tossed together. Draw a tree diagram to show the probabilities and use it to find the probability of getting:

(a) exactly one head,

(b) at least one head.

11 When Ms Thomas reaches her place of work the probability that she can get a lift on the ground floor immediately is $\frac{1}{5}$ and the probability that she can get a different lift straightaway from the sixth floor to the tenth floor is $\frac{1}{3}$. Find the probability that:

(a) she has to wait for just one of these lifts,

(b) she does not have to wait for either.

12 In a game of chance on a machine a player may win with a probability of $\frac{1}{8}$, lose with a probability of $\frac{1}{2}$, or draw. He continues playing for another game if he draws but not otherwise.

(a) The tree diagram shows all the possible outcomes for up to three games. Copy the diagram and fill in the missing probabilities.

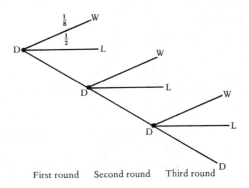

First round   Second round   Third round

(b) Calculate the probability that the player:
   (i) will win after exactly two games,
  (ii) will win after exactly three games,
 (iii) will win after three or fewer games,
 (iv) can continue playing after three games.

Statistics

1 The pie chart represents the places of manufacture of all the cars in a car park.

  (a) If there were 86 Japanese cars how many were manufactured:
    (i) in the United Kingdom,   (ii) in Europe?

  (b) What percentage of the cars were manufactured in the United Kingdom?

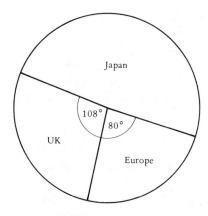

2 A fifth-form student spent three hours revising her science subjects for the end of term examinations. The pie chart shows how this time was divided among the subjects. How much time was spent revising:

  (a) chemistry,   (b) physics?

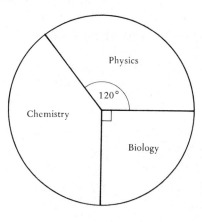

3   The pie chart shows the comparative profits of the four companies A, B, C and D that form a group. If B's profit is £127 500 find:

(a) the total profit for the group,

(b) A's profit as a percentage of C's.

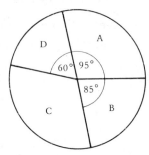

4   Two hundred fourth-form students were required to choose one subject from an option group with four subjects. The numbers choosing each subject were: geography 56, chemistry 30, woodwork 24, art 90. Draw a pie diagram to illustrate this data.

5   For every pound collected by Westshire County Council the breakdown is: government grants 45p, rents 20p, local taxes 25p, charges 10p. Draw a pie diagram to illustrate this data.

6   Paula's take-home pay is £180 per week. She spends £32 on rent, £28 on food, £24 on travel, £12 on heat and light, £34 on clothes and entertainment, and saves the remainder.

(a) How much does she save each week?

(b) Draw a pie chart to illustrate this information.

7   A department store employs 63 men and 104 women. The total wages bill for one week is £10 672. If the mean weekly wage for the men is £72, calculate the mean weekly wage for the women.

8   In ten consecutive games the results of Liverpool's matches were as follows: 1–0, 2–1, 0–0, 3–0, 1–2, 1–1, 1–0, 2–0, 5–1, 2–1. Find the average 'goals for' and 'goals against'.

9   The heights of six boys in a team are 153 cm, 149 cm, 163 cm, 160 cm, 147 cm and 158 cm. Find the average (mean) height of the boys.

Five other boys whose average height is 160 cm combine with the six to form a football team. Find:

(a) the total of the heights of the five new boys,

(b) the average height of the whole team, giving your answer correct to one decimal place.

10 Peter's parents promise him £5 if his mean (average) mark for the eight examinations he is about to sit is *more than* 60. After seven examinations his average mark is 58. What is the lowest mark he can score in the final examination if he is to receive his £5 'reward'?

11 A page from an Ian Fleming novel was chosen at random and the number of letters in each of the first fifty words on that page was recorded.

$$
\begin{array}{cccccccccc}
3 & 5 & 5 & 9 & 2 & 7 & 3 & 6 & 5 & 4 \\
7 & 3 & 5 & 4 & 4 & 2 & 6 & 3 & 8 & 5 \\
4 & 1 & 4 & 2 & 10 & 5 & 4 & 5 & 7 & 3 \\
6 & 3 & 8 & 5 & 2 & 3 & 6 & 4 & 2 & 3 \\
8 & 7 & 3 & 3 & 4 & 5 & 5 & 2 & 3 & 8
\end{array}
$$

Copy and complete the following table.

No. of letters	Tally	Frequency
0		
1		
2		
3		
4		
5		
6		
7		
8		
9		
10		

Find the mean, modal and median number of letters per word.

12 A six-sided die was thrown 100 times. The table gives the number of times each score was obtained.

Score	1	2	3	4	5	6
Frequency	16	20	13	16	11	24

Find the mean, mode and median for these data.

13 The first ten customers at a supermarket one day spent the following amounts: £4.36, £12.84, £13.16, £9.27, £1.49, £20.82, £33.24, £24.19, £29.74, £10.89. Find the mean and median amount spent.

14 The pupils in a class were each asked how many brothers and/or sisters they had. The results are illustrated in the diagram.

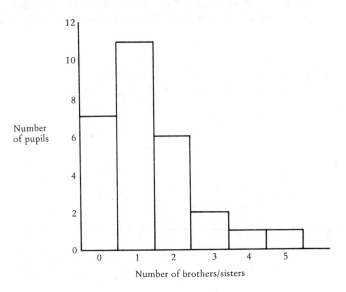

(a) How many pupils had exactly one brother or sister?

(b) How many pupils were there in the class?

(c) How many pupils had two or more brothers/sisters?

(d) What is the modal number of brothers/sisters?

(e) Calculate the mean number of children for the families to which the children in this class belonged (take care!).

15 A group of smokers, who attended a working men's club, were asked to record the number of cigarettes they smoked each day for a fortnight. The table below is based on this information.

Average no. of cigarettes smoked per day	1–5	6–10	11–20	21–30
No. of smokers	8	12	30	21

Average no. of cigarettes smoked per day	31–40	41–60	61–80
No. of smokers	12	14	6

(a) How many smokers took part?

(b) Illustrate these data on a histogram.

16 The table shows the masses (kg) and heights (cm) of ten boys.

Boy	A	B	C	D	E	F	G	H	I	J
Mass (in kg)	58	80	45	52	74	70	65	47	84	60
Height (in cm)	158	192	138	152	180	150	156	144	190	170

On a graph draw a scatter diagram for this information. Use 2 cm to represent 10 kg on the horizontal axis and 1 cm to represent 10 cm on the vertical axis.

(a) By eye, draw a line of best fit.

(b) Use your line to estimate (i) the mass of a boy who is 164 cm tall, (ii) the height of a boy who has a mass of 77 kg.

(c) Find the gradient of your straight line.

(d) If D grows 10 cm by how much would you expect his mass to increase?

(e) Which boy is obviously overweight for his height?

17 The table shows the prices of some school text books and the number of pages in them.

Book	A	B	C	D	E
Price (in £s)	4	6.20	3.20	5.30	6.90
No. of pages	325	375	205	375	460

Book	F	G	H	I	J
Price (in £s)	5.90	3.80	6.50	6	4.70
No. of pages	405	225	445	350	275

On graph paper draw a scatter diagram for this information. Use 2 cm to represent £1 on the horizontal axis and 2 cm to represent 50 pages on the vertical axis.

(a) By eye, draw a line of best fit.

(b) Use your straight line to estimate:
    (i) the cost of a book with 250 pages,
    (ii) the number of pages I could expect to find in a book costing £5.

(c) Find the gradient of your straight line. Can you attach a meaning to this value?

(d) Which book appears to provide the best value for money?

18 Five hundred pupils sat an examination. Their marks are summarised in the table.

Mark	⩽ 20	⩽ 30	⩽ 40	⩽ 50	⩽ 60
No. of candidates	45	105	300	390	434

Mark	⩽ 70	⩽ 80	⩽ 90	⩽ 100
No. of candidates	462	480	494	500

(a) Draw a cumulative frequency curve to represent these results. Use a scale of 1 cm to represent 10 marks on the horizontal axis and 1 cm to represent 25 pupils on the vertical axis.

(b) Use your curve to find:
   (i) the number of pupils who scored 58 or less,
   (ii) the median mark,
   (iii) the interquartile range,
   (iv) the percentage of pupils who scored more than 46 marks,
   (v) the minimum mark required to pass, if 80% passed.

19 The prices of 300 houses offered for sale in a local paper during a certain week are summarised in the following table.

Price (in £s)	0–	10 000–	20 000–	25 000–	30 000–
Frequency	0	2	7	42	87

Price (in £s)	35 000–	40 000–	45 000–	50 000–
Frequency	81	30	12	12

Price (in £s)	55 000–	75 000–90 000
Frequency	12	15

(10 000– means £10 000 or more but less than £20 000.)

(a) Represent this information in a histogram, using class boundaries 0, 10 000, 20 000, 25 000, etc.

(b) Use the given table to draw up a table of cumulative frequencies and hence draw a cumulative frequency curve.
(Use 2 cm to represent £10 000 on the horizontal axis and 4 cm to represent 50 houses on the vertical axis.)

(c) Use your graph to estimate (i) the median, (ii) the upper and lower quartiles, of this distribution.

(d) The maximum that a married couple can afford for a house is £38 500. Estimate the percentage of the 300 houses that are within their price range.

74

20 The table shows the distribution of the ages on 1 January of the pupils in an 11–18 school.

Age	11+	12+	13+	14+	15+	16+	17+	18+
No. of pupils	130	210	200	195	216	158	66	26

(The group 11+ means pupils who have had their 11th birthday but have not reached their 12th birthday.)

Copy and complete the following cumulative frequency table and use it to draw a cumulative frequency curve.

Age	<12	<13	<14	<15	<16	<17	<18	<19
No. of pupils								

Hence find:
(a) the number of pupils in the school,
(b) the median age,
(c) the interquartile range for this data.

Variation   21

1 Express the following sentences as mathematical equations:
   (a) P varies directly as Q,
   (b) H varies directly as the square of t,
   (c) y varies inversely as the square root of x,
   (d) p varies inversely as q.

2 If y varies as x and $y = 12$ when $x = 3$, find:
   (a) y when $x = 4$ (b) x when $y = 6$

3 If p varies as q and $p = 10$ when $q = 100$ find:
   (a) p when $q = 20$ (b) q when $p = 3$

4 If y varies as the square of x and $y = 80$ when $x = 4$, find:
   (a) y when $x = 8$ (b) x when $y = 125$

5 If p varies as the square of q and $p = 8$ when $q = 4$ find:
   (a) p when $q = 3$ (b) q when $p = 32$

6 If y varies as the cube of x and $y = 27$ when $x = \frac{3}{2}$ find:
   (a) y when $x = 2$ (b) x when $y = 125$

7   If y varies as the square root of x and $y = 6$ when $x = 4$ find:
    (a) y when $x = 25$ (b) x when $y = 3$

8   If y varies as $(5x + 2)$ and $y = 4$ when $x = 2$ find:
    (a) y when $x = 5$ (b) x when $y = 1$

9   If the cube of y varies as x and $y = 2$ when $x = 1$ find:
    (a) x when $y = 3$ (b) y when $x = 27$

10 Given that the square of x varies as y, and that $x = 2$ when $y = \frac{1}{2}$
    find:
    (a) y when $x = 10$ (b) x when $y = \frac{8}{9}$

11 If y varies as the square root of $(2x + 1)$ and $x = 24$ when $y = 63$
    find:
    (a) x when $y = 27$ (b) y when $x = 12$

12 Two variables p and q are such that $ap + bq = 0$ where a and b are

    constants. If $p = 4$ when $q = 3$ find $\dfrac{a}{b}$ and hence find:

    (a) p when $q = 10$ (b) q when $p = -4$

13 The following table shows some values of the variables x and y which
    are connected by the equation $y = 4x^n$.

x	$\frac{1}{4}$	4	9
y	2	8	12

    (a) Find the value of n.
    (b) Find y when (i) $x = 1$ (ii) $x = 16$.
    (c) Find x when (i) $y = 20$ (ii) $y = \frac{8}{3}$.
    (d) Express x in terms of y.

14 The following table shows some values of the variables x and y which
    are connected by the equation $y = 9x^n$.

x	$\frac{1}{8}$	1	27
y	18	9	3

    (a) Find the value of n.
    (b) Find y when $x = 8$.
    (c) Find x when $y = 13\frac{1}{2}$.
    (d) Express x in terms of y.

15 The volume (V) of a solid with a circular base varies directly as its height (H) and as the square of the radius of its base (R). When the height is 4 cm and the radius of the base is 2.5 cm, the volume of the solid is 50 cm³. Find:

(a) the formula connecting V, R and H,

(b) the value of V when $R = 5$ cm and $H = 4$ cm,

(c) the value of R when $V = 72$ cm³ and $H = 4$ cm.

16 The volume of a gas is inversely proportional to its pressure. When the pressure is 30 cm of mercury the volume is 600 cm³. Find:

(a) the pressure when the volume is 250 cm³,

(b) the volume when the pressure is 45 cm of mercury.

17 The number of uniform spherical shot that can be made from a given mass of lead varies inversely as the cube of the radius of the shot required. When the radius is 1 mm the number of shot is 2744. How many shot of radius 1.4 mm may be made from the given mass?

18 The capacity (C) of a set of similar jugs varies as the cube of their heights (H). If a jug which is 20 cm high holds one litre find the capacity of a jug which is:

(a) 12 cm high,   (b) 24 cm high.

19 The heat produced in a wire (H) varies directly as the square of the current (I), and as the time (T) for which the current flows. When a current of 3 amps flows for 5 minutes, 1620 joules of heat are produced. Find the heat produced when 5 amps flows through the same resistance for 8 minutes.

20 The volume (V) of a right circular cone varies as its height (H) and as the square of its radius (R). Find the percentage increase in the volume of a cone if its radius increases by 20% and its height by 25%.

21 The period of oscillation of a simple pendulum varies directly as the square root of its length. If the period is 2.4 seconds when the length is 144 cm, find:

(a) the period when the length is 100 cm,

(b) the length when the period is 1.8 seconds.

22 The resistance (R) of a wire varies as the length (L) of the wire and inversely as the square of its diameter (D). If the resistance of 1 kilometre of copper wire 2 mm in diameter is 23 ohms find the resistance of 6.9 kilometres of similar wire with diameter 2.3 mm.

23 Kepler's third law states that the squares of the periodic times of the planets are proportional to the cubes of their mean distances from the Sun. Given that the mean distance of the Earth from the Sun is 92 million miles and that of Mars is 140 million miles, how long does Mars take to travel round the Sun?

24 The force (F) acting on a mass moving in a circle varies directly as the square of its speed (v) and inversely as the radius of the circle (r) in which it moves. Find the increase (or decrease) in the force F if:

(a) the speed is doubled and the radius halved,

(b) the speed is halved and the radius doubled.

Trigonometry in Two- and Three-Dimensions

22

In this exercise give all the angles correct to the nearest tenth of a degree and all distances correct to three significant figures.

1

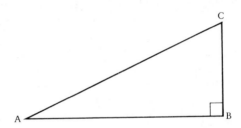

Use the diagram to find (i) BC (ii) AB, if:

(a) AC = 10 cm and $\widehat{A} = 32°$ (b) AC = 30 cm and $\widehat{A} = 55°$

(c) AC = 12 cm and $\widehat{A} = 46°$ (d) AC = 8 cm and $\widehat{C} = 60°$

(e) AC = 6 cm and $\widehat{C} = 42°$ (f) AC = 14 cm and $\widehat{C} = 73°$

2

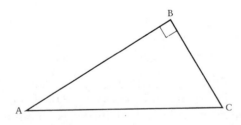

Use the diagram to find:

(a) BC if AB = 12 cm and $B\widehat{A}C = 48°$

(b) BC if AC = 8 cm and $B\widehat{A}C = 36°$

(c) AB if AC = 6 cm and $B\widehat{C}A = 54°$

(d) AB if BC = 9 cm and $B\widehat{C}A = 47°$

78

3

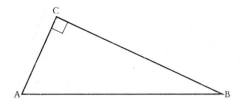

Use the diagram to find:

(a) AB if BC = 6 cm and $\widehat{A} = 64°$

(b) AC if BC = 8 cm and $\widehat{B} = 47°$

(c) AB if AC = 9 cm and $\widehat{A} = 74°$

(d) BC if AB = 16 cm and $\widehat{B} = 38°$

4

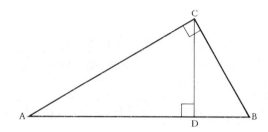

Use the diagram to find:

(a) AB and BC if AC = 12 cm and $\widehat{A} = 38°$

(b) AD and DC if AC = 8 cm and $\widehat{A} = 44°$

(c) BC and CD if BD = 6 cm and $\widehat{B} = 68°$

(d) AC and AB if CD = 5 cm and $\widehat{ACD} = 56°$

5

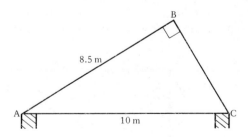

The diagram shows the cross-section of a factory roof. The span AC is 10 metres and AB is 8.5 metres. Calculate:

(a) the inclination of AB to the horizontal,

(b) the length BC,

(c) the area of triangle ABC.

6

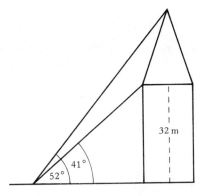

32 m

41°
52°

A church tower 32 metres high is surmounted by a vertical spire. From a point on the ground, in the horizontal plane through the base of the tower, the angles of elevation of the base and top of the spire are 41° and 52° respectively. How tall is the spire? (Neglect the width of the tower.)

7 A man walks 70 metres away from the base of a vertical building and finds that the elevation of its top is 30°. How high is the building? He continues his walk away from the building in the same straight line until he reaches another point from which the elevation of the top is 25°. How far has he walked from the foot of the building?

8

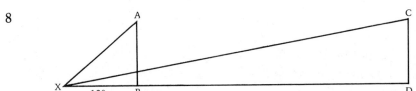

A
C
X
120 m
B
D

The diagram shows the two similar supporting towers of a suspension bridge. When the tops of the towers A and C are viewed from a point X, situated 120 m from the base of AB such that XBD are in a horizontal straight line, their angles of elevation are 39.8° and 6.2° respectively. Calculate the heights of the towers and the horizontal distance between them, giving your answers correct to the nearest metre.

9

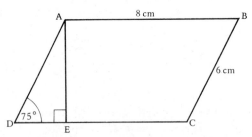

A
8 cm
B
6 cm
75°
D
E
C

ABCD is a parallelogram with E the foot of the perpendicular from A to DC. If AB = 8 cm, BC = 6 cm and $\widehat{ADE} = 75°$ calculate:
(a) AE,   (b) DE,   (c) the area of the parallelogram.

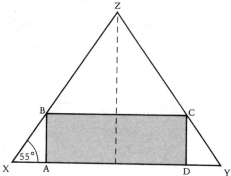

The diagram shows the cross-section of a roof XYZ, the shaded area ABCD representing the cross-section of a room within the roof space. If $ZX = ZY = 7\frac{1}{2}$ metres, $\angle ZXY = 55°$ and $\dfrac{XB}{BZ} = \dfrac{2}{3}$ find:

(a) the height of the ridge Z above XY,

(b) the width of the roof XY,

(c) the height (AB) and the width (AD) of the room.

11 A and B are two look-out posts on the opposite sides of a river with parallel banks. The river flows north-south and at 1 p.m. a ship S is in a direction N21°E (021°) from A while it is 1600 metres from B in a direction N40°W (320°). Find the width of the river.

If the ship moves at $10 \, \text{km h}^{-1}$ in a direction parallel to the bank of the river, at what time will it be immediately opposite A and B?

12 At 3 p.m. a liner is at A, 4 nautical miles due North of a lightship S. The liner maintains a constant speed on a bearing of 120° and reaches a point B, due East of the lightship at 3.24 p.m. If C is the point on the liner's path which is nearest to S:

(a) Draw a sketch to show the positions of A, B, C and S.

(b) Calculate the distances AB and CS.

(c) Find the speed of the liner.

13

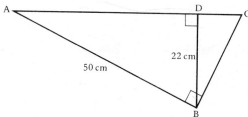

ABC represents the cross-section through a horse-trough which is 2 metres long. $\angle ABC = 90°$, $AB = 50 \, \text{cm}$ and the depth of the trough at its deepest point is 22 cm. Calculate:

(a) the width of the trough AC,

(b) the length of the other sloping side BC,

(c) the volume, in m^3, contained in the trough when full.

14

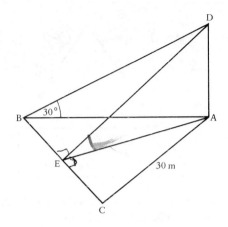

A vertical flagpole stands at A, one corner of a horizontal equilateral triangle ABC of side 30 metres. From B the elevation of the top of the flagpole D is 30°. How high is the pole? If E is the midpoint of BC, find AE and the elevation of the top of the pole from E.

15

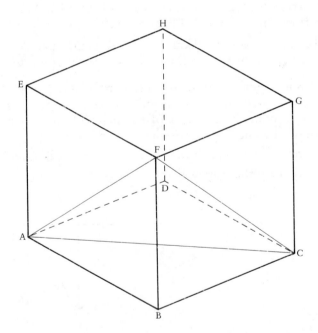

ABCDEFGH is a cube of side 10 cm.

(a) Calculate the lengths of AC, AF and CF. Hence draw the triangle ACF accurately and find its area.

(b) What name is given to the solid ABCF?

(c) Draw a net for this solid.

16

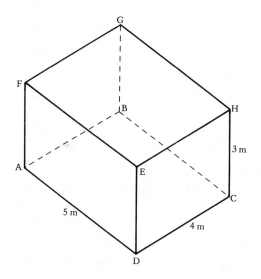

The diagram represents a room measuring 5 m × 4 m × 3 m. Find:
(a) the angle between AE and the floor,
(b) the angle between AH and the floor,
(c) the angle between the two diagonals AH and CF.

17

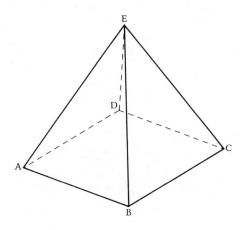

ABCDE is a pyramid with a square base. All its edges are 8 cm long. Find:
(a) the length of AC,
(b) angle AEC,
(c) the height of E above the base ABCD,
(d) the volume of the pyramid.

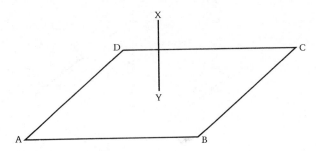

18

A flagpole XY, 10 m high, stands at the centre of a square courtyard with side 30 metres. A man, whose eyes are 2 m above the ground, stands at:

(a) the corner A,

(b) the midpoint of the side AB,

(c) the point of trisection of AB nearer to A.

In each case calculate the angle of elevation of the top of the flagpole.

Graphs 23

1 The graph shows Harriet's mass during the first twenty years of her life.

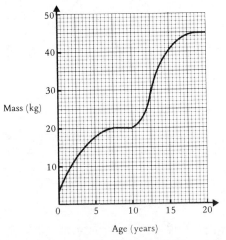

(a) When were Harriet's main growing times?

(b) When did she not grow at all?

(c) At what age did she finish growing?

(d) What would probably happen to her mass during the next twenty years?

2 Penny went into hospital. Her temperature chart for the six days she stayed is reproduced below.

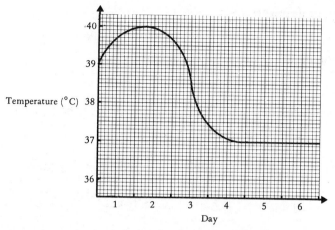

(a) On which day was Penny's temperature highest?
(b) What do you think is Penny's normal temperature?
(c) On which day did her temperature return to normal?

3 The masses of ball-bearings of various diameters were as follows.

Diameter, D (in mm)	5	10	15	20	25	28
Mass, m (in grams)	0.5	5.5	18	42	82	115

Draw a graph to illustrate these data using $3\,cm \equiv 5\,mm$ on the D-axis and $2\,cm \equiv 10\,g$ on the m-axis. Use your graph to estimate:
(a) the diameter of a ball-bearing of mass $100\,g$,
(b) the mass of a ball-bearing of diameter $18\,mm$.

4 The depth of water in a harbour at different times is shown in the following table.

Time	6 a.m.	7 a.m.	8 a.m.	9 a.m.	10 a.m.
Depth of water (in metres)	5.1	3.8	3.1	3.2	3.7

Time	11 a.m.	Noon	1 p.m.	2 p.m.	3 p.m.
Depth of water (in metres)	4.7	6.3	8.0	8.9	8.9

Time	4 p.m.	5 p.m.	6 p.m.
Depth of water (in metres)	8.4	7.3	5.3

Draw a graph to represent these data using $2 \, cm \equiv 1 \, hour$ for the horizontal time axis and $2 \, cm \equiv 1 \, metre$ for the vertical depth axis.

Use your graph to find:

(a) the times when the depth of water is 7 metres,

(b) the depth of water at 10.30 a.m.

5   The time of sunrise at Greenwich on various dates, each two weeks apart, is given in the following table.

Date, D	March 28	April 11	25	May 9	23
Time, T	6.45	6.15	5.45	5.18	4.57

Date, D	June 6	20	July 4	18
Time, T	4.45	4.42	4.51	5.03

Using $1 \, cm \equiv 1 \, week$ on the D-axis and $4 \, cm \equiv 1 \, hour$ on the T-axis, plot these points and join them with a smooth curve. From the graph determine:

(a) the time of sunrise on 16 May,

(b) on which date the sun rises at 6.00 a.m.

6   A packaging manufacturer produces rectangular cardboard boxes of varying depths but always with the sides in the same proportions. The area of cardboard used for boxes of different depths is given in the table.

Depth of box, D (in cm)	10	15	20	25	30	35	40
Area of cardboard, A (in m²)	0.09	0.20	0.36	0.56	0.81	1.10	1.44

Taking $6 \, cm \equiv 10 \, units$ on the horizontal D-axis and $10 \, cm$ as 1 unit on the vertical A-axis draw a graph to represent these data and use it to find:

(a) the depth of the box made from 1 m² of cardboard,

(b) the area of cardboard used to make a box with a depth of 22 cm.

86

7   A river is 70 metres wide. The table shows the depth of water in the river at different distances from one bank.

Distance from bank, S (in metres)	0	10	20	30	40	50	60	65	70
Depth of water, D (in metres)	0	2.2	4	5.6	6.8	7	6	4	0

Taking $4\,cm \equiv 10$ metres for S and $2\,cm \equiv 1$ metre for D, draw a graph to represent these data and use it to estimate:
(a) the depth 25 metres from the bank,
(b) where the river is 5 metres deep,
(c) the distance from the bank where the river has its maximum depth.

8

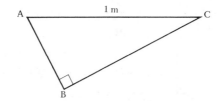

The diagram shows the cross-section of a farmyard water trough. The manufacturer wishes to produce a trough that is one metre wide (i.e. AC = 1 m) and always has a base angle of 90°. Copy and complete the following table which gives the values of AB, BC and the area of triangle ABC, for different values of $\widehat{ACB}$.

Angle $\widehat{ACB}$	Length of AB, L (in m)	Length of BC, B (in m)	Area of triangle ABC, A (in m²)
10°	0.17	0.98	0.083
20°	0.34	0.94	0.160
30°	0.5	0.87	0.218
40°	0.64	0.77	0.246
50°	0.77	0.64	0.246
60°			
70°			
80°			

Draw a graph, plotting values of A against the corresponding values of L. Take 2 cm to represent 0.1 m on the L-axis and 4 cm to represent 0.1 m² on the A-axis.

Use your graph to find:
(a) the value of AB when the area of ABC is 0.2 m²,
(b) the maximum value for the area of triangle ABC and the corresponding value of AB.

87

9. An open rectangular box of length l cm is to have square ends of side a cm. The sum of the length and girth of the box is to be 52 cm, i.e. $l + 4a = 52$. Copy and complete the table given below, which shows different values for a and the corresponding values for l; and the capacity of the box C, in cubic centimetres, where $C = a^2 l$.

Side of square, a (in cm)	0	1	2	3	4	5	6
Length of box, l (in cm)	52		44	40	36		
Capacity, C (in cm³)	0		176	360	576		

Side of square, a (in cm)	7	8	9	10	11	12	13
Length of box, l (in cm)	24	20	16	12	8	4	0
Capacity, C (in cm³)	1176	1280	1296	1200	968	576	0

Draw the graph of C against a. Use 2 cm to represent 1 unit on the a-axis and 1 cm to represent 100 units on the C-axis. Use your graph to find:

(a) the value(s) of a when the capacity is 900 cm³,

(b) the largest possible capacity and the value of a for which it occurs.

10 The sketch shows the graph of $y = x^2 - x - 6$.

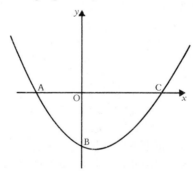

(a) Find the coordinates of A, B and C.

(b) Find the equation of the straight line joining B and C.

(c) Copy the sketch and draw in the graph of $y = x - 3$. Let this graph intersect the given graph at D and E.

What equation will have the x-coordinates of D and E as roots?

88

11   The equation of the curve shown in the sketch is:

$$y = p + qx - x^2$$

Find:

(a) the values of p and q,   (b) the coordinates of A.

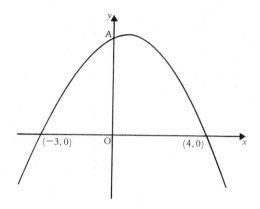

12   On the same axes, sketch the graphs of $y = x^2$, $y = x^2 + 4$, $y = x^2 - 4$, $y = 4 - x^2$, clearly distinguishing between them.

13   Sketch the graph of $y = 5 + 4x - x^2$, showing clearly where it crosses the axes. On the same axes sketch the graphs of:

(a) $y = 4x - x^2$ (b) $y = x^2 - 4x - 5$

14   (a) Factorise $x^2 - 7x + 12$.

(b) Solve the equation $x^2 - 7x + 12 = 0$.

(c) The sketch shows the graph of $y = x^2 - 7x + 12$. Write down the coordinates of the points marked A, B and C.

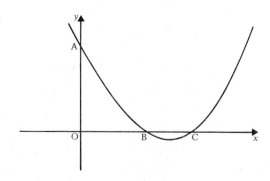

(d) Copy the sketch and draw the line of symmetry for this curve. What is the equation of this line? Write down the coordinates of the point where the line of symmetry crosses the curve.

15 The sketch shows the graph of the quadratic curve given by the equation $y = x^2 + bx + c$.

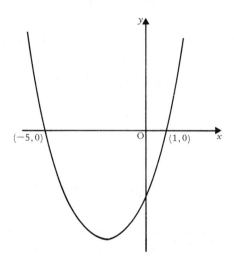

(a) Find the values of b and c.

(b) What is the equation of the axis of symmetry for this curve?

(c) What are the coordinates of the point where the curve crosses the y-axis?

(d) Calculate the values of x for which y is 7.

16 (a) Factorise $3 + 5x - 2x^2$.

(b) Solve the equation $3 + 5x - 2x^2 = 0$.

(c) The sketch shows the graph of $y = 3 + 5x - 2x^2$. Write down the coordinates of A, B and C.

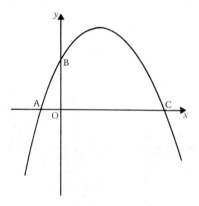

(d) Copy the sketch and draw the axis of symmetry for this quadratic curve. Write down the equation of this line.

17 Draw the graph of $y = x^2$ for values of x from -4 to 4 at half-unit intervals. Take 2 cm as 1 unit for x and 1 cm as 1 unit for y.

What straight-line graphs would it be necessary to draw, in conjunction with the graph of $y = x^2$, to solve each of the following equations?

(a) $x^2 = 6$

(b) $x^2 - 2x - 6 = 0$

(c) $2x^2 - x - 6 = 0$

Draw the appropriate graphs and hence solve the three given equations.

18 Draw the graph of $y = x^2 - 3x - 5$ for whole number values of x from -2 to 5. Take 2 cm as 1 unit for x and 1 cm as 1 unit for y.

Use your graph to find the lowest value of $x^2 - 3x - 5$ and the corresponding value of x. Draw, on the same axes, the graph of $y = x - 3$.

(a) Use your graph to solve the equations:
    (i) $x^2 - 3x - 5 = 0$ (ii) $x^2 - 3x - 8 = 0$

(b) Write down the values of x at the points of intersection of the two graphs.

(c) Use your graph to find the range of values of x for which $x^2 - 3x - 5$ is less than $x - 3$.

(d) Find, in its simplest form, the equation whose roots are the values of x at the points of intersection of the two graphs.

19 Complete the table below for $y = x^2 - 3x - 4$.

x	-2	-1	0	1	2	3	4	5
x^2	4	1		1		9		25
$-3x$	6	3		-3		-9		-15
-4	-4	-4		-4		-4		-4
y	6			-6				6

(a) Draw the graph of $y = x^2 - 3x - 4$ for values of x from -2 to 5. Take 2 cm as 1 unit on both axes.

(b) Draw and label the line of symmetry for this curve. Write down the equation of this line.

91

20 Complete the following table which gives values of $12 - 2x - 3x^2$ for values of x between -4 and $+4$.

x	-4	-3	-2	-1	0
12 $-2x$ $-3x^2$	12 8 -48	12 6 -27	12 -12	12 2 -3	12
$12 - 2x - 3x^2$	-28	-9		11	

x	1	2	3	$3\frac{1}{2}$	4
12 $-2x$ $-3x^2$	12 -2 -3	12 -4	12 -6 -27	12 -7 $-36\frac{3}{4}$	12 -8 -48
$12 - 2x - 3x^2$	7		-19	$-31\frac{1}{4}$	-44

Taking $2\,\text{cm} \equiv 1$ unit on the x-axis and $2\,\text{cm} \equiv 5$ units on the y-axis plot the graph of $y = 12 - 2x - 3x^2$.

Use your graph to:

(a) find the values of x which make $12 - 2x - 3x^2 = 0$,

(b) estimate the maximum value of $12 - 2x - 3x^2$ and the value of x for which this maximum occurs.

21

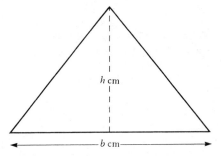

The sum of the height, h cm, and the base, b cm of an isosceles triangle is 20 cm. Show that the area of this triangle, A cm², is given by the equation $A = \frac{1}{2}b(20 - b)$.

Draw the graph of $A = \frac{1}{2}b(20 - b)$ for values of b from 0 to 20. Take 4 cm as 5 units on the b-axis and 2 cm as 5 cm² on the A-axis.

Use your graph to find:

(a) the value(s) of b that gives an area of 37 cm²,

(b) the area when the base is 13.5 cm,

(c) the maximum value for the area and the length of the base for which this maximum area occurs.

22   Write down the three values missing from the following table, which gives values of $x^3 - 3x^2$ for values of x in the range 0 to 3.5.

x	0	0.5	1	1.5	2	2.5	3	3.25	3.5
$x^3 - 3x^2$	0	-0.625		-3.375		-3.125	0	2.64	

Using 4 cm as 1 unit on the x-axis and 2 cm as 1 unit on the y-axis, draw the graph of $y = x^3 - 3x^2$.

By drawing suitable straight lines on your graph:

(a) Estimate the gradient of the curve $y = x^3 - 3x^2$ at the point $(2.5, -3.125)$.

(b) Find two solutions of the equation:

$$x^3 - 3x^2 = x - 2$$

23   Draw the graph of $y = \dfrac{8}{x}$ for values of x between 1 and 8, taking 2 cm as 1 unit on each axis. On the same axes draw the graph of $y = \frac{4}{3}(6 - x)$. Hence write down:

(a) the range of values of x for which $\frac{1}{3}(6 - x) > \dfrac{2}{x}$,

(b) the values of x at the points of intersection of the two graphs,

(c) the equation, in its simplest form, for which these intersection values of x are the roots.

24   Write down the three values missing from the following table which gives values of $\dfrac{7}{x} + 2$ for values of x from 1 to 8.

x	1	$1\frac{1}{2}$	2	3	4	5	6	7	8
$\dfrac{7}{x} + 2$	9		$5\frac{1}{2}$	$4\frac{1}{3}$	$3\frac{3}{4}$		$3\frac{1}{6}$		$2\frac{7}{8}$

Using the same axes, draw the graphs of $y = \dfrac{7}{x} + 2$ and $y = 8 - x$ for values of x from 1 to 8 taking 2 cm as 1 unit on each axis.

Use your graphs to write down the range of values of x for which $\dfrac{7}{x} + 2 < 8 - x$.

Write down the values of x where the graphs intersect. Write down, and simplify, the equation which is satisfied by the values of x at these intersection points.

25   When a ship travels at v knots (nautical miles per hour), the cost of a journey of 100 nautical miles is $£\left(\dfrac{1800}{v} + 20v\right)$.

Complete the following table which shows the cost in pounds (c) for values of v from 5 to 12.

Speed in knots, v	5	6	7	8	9	10	11	12
Cost in pounds, c	460	420	397		380		383	

Draw a graph to show how the cost varies for speeds between 5 knots and 12 knots. Take 2 cm to represent 1 knot, and 2 cm to represent £20. Scale the c-axis from 300 to 480.

Use your graph to estimate:

(a) the cost of the journey at a speed of 6.4 knots,

(b) the speed at which the cost of the journey will be £425,

(c) the speed at which the cost of the journey is least.

26   An open rectangular box of volume 32 cm³ has a base in the form of a square of side x cm. Express the height of the box in terms of x and hence show that the total surface area (A) of the outside of the box is given by $A = \left(x^2 + \dfrac{128}{x}\right)$ cm².

Complete the following table which gives values for x and the corresponding values of A.

x	1.5	2	2.5	3	3.5	4	4.5	5
A	87.6		57.5	51.7	48.8		48.7	

Taking 4 cm as 1 unit on the x-axis and as 20 units on the A-axis, draw a graph to show how A changes as x varies from 1.5 to 5.

Use your graph to estimate:

(a) the minimum value of A,

(b) the side of the largest base which will give a total surface area of 50 cm²,

(c) the total surface area when the base has side 1.7 cm.

94

27 Complete the following tables which give values for sin x (correct to two decimal places) between $x = 0°$ and $x = 180°$. Using $1\,\text{cm} \equiv 10°$ for x and $2\,\text{cm} \equiv 0.1$ for y plot the graph of $y = \sin x$ over the given range.

x	0°	10°	20°	30°	40°	50°	60°	70°	80°	90°
sin x	0	0.17	0.34	0.50		0.77	0.87	0.94	0.98	1.00

x	100°	110°	120°	130°	140°	150°	160°	170°	180°
sin x	0.98	0.94	0.87		0.64	0.50		0.17	0

Use your graph to find:

(a) sin 55° and sin 155°,

(b) the angle(s) whose sine is 0.7

Loci   24

1

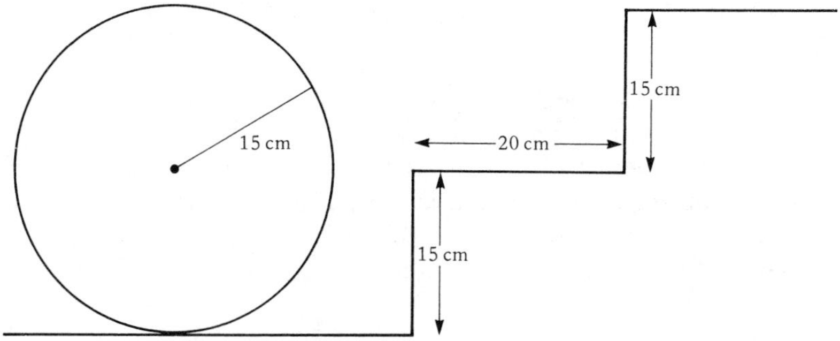

A wheel of radius 15 cm rolls across a horizontal path and then up two steps, each 15 cm high and 20 cm apart, before continuing to roll horizontally. Sketch the locus of the centre of the wheel.

2 A and B are two points 8 cm apart. Draw accurately the sets $X = \{P : PA = PB\}$ and $Y = \{Q : AQ = 5\,\text{cm}\}$. If $X \cap Y = \{M, N\}$ mark the points M and N on your diagram and construct the circle that passes through B, M and N. Measure and record the radius of this circle.

3   ABCD is a square plot of ground of side 50 m.

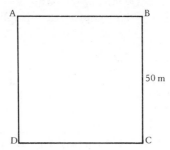

(a) Shade the region that satisfies both the following conditions:
    (i) each point in the region is further from A than from B,
    (ii) each point in the region is nearer to C than to A.
(b) Calculate the area of the shaded region.

4

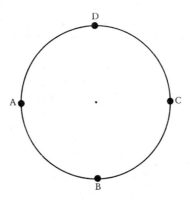

The diagram shows a circular area of sea, of diameter 15 km. A, B, C
and D are four ships equally spaced around the circumference of the
circle. An enemy submarine is known to be resting within the circle
and soundings show that it is more than 7 km from A and more than
10 km from B. Make a scale drawing, using 1 cm to represent 1 km,
and shade the area within which the submarine lies.

5

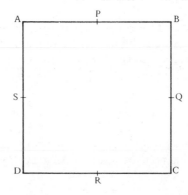

The diagram opposite shows a square vegetable plot ABCD of side 20 m. P, Q, R and S are the midpoints of the sides. The gardener wishes to plant a tree satisfying the following conditions:

(a) it is nearer to A than it is to C,

(b) it is further from A than P is from A.

Make a scale drawing and shade the area within which the tree must be planted.

6

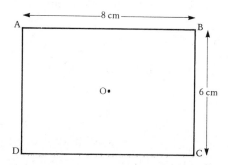

O is the point of intersection of the diagonals AC and BD of a rectangle ABCD in which AB = 8 cm and BC = 6 cm.

(a) Describe the locus of A as the rectangle is rotated about O.

(b) Describe the locus of O as the rectangle is rotated about A.

(c) Describe the locus of A as the rectangle is rotated about B.

(d) Describe the locus of A as the rectangle is rotated about BC through 360°.

7

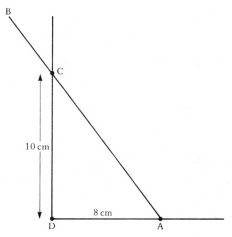

AB represents the stay on the drop down front of a writing desk. The stay is fixed to the front at A and passes through a fixed slot at C. If AB = 15 cm, AD = 8 cm and CD = 10 cm draw an accurate diagram with the front in the horizontal position shown in the diagram and plot different positions of B as the front closes, about the hinge at D, 10° at a time.

Sets

1 If $A = \{2,3,4,5,6,7\}$ and $B = \{2,4,6,8\}$ write down the elements of:

(a) $A \cup B$ (b) $A \cap B$

2 If $X = \{v, w\}$, $Y = \{w, x, y\}$ are subsets of the universal set $\{v,w,x,y,z\}$ write down the elements in each of the following sets:

(a) X' (b) $X \cap Y$ (c) $X \cup Y'$

3 X, Y and Z are subsets of the universal set $\mathcal{E} = \{1,2,3,4,\ldots 15\}$. If:

$$X = \{x : x \text{ is a factor of } 30\}$$
$$Y = \{x : x \text{ is a factor of } 42\}$$
$$Z = \{x : x \text{ is a factor of } 56\}$$

(a) Illustrate this information on a Venn diagram,

(b) List the elements in the set $X \cap (Y \cup Z)'$.

4 P and Q are subsets of the universal set $\mathcal{E} = \{1,2,3,4,5,6,7,8,9\}$.

If $P = \{\text{prime numbers}\}$, $Q = \{\text{odd numbers}\}$, list the elements of:

(a) $P \cap Q'$ (b) $P' \cap Q$ (c) $(P \cap Q') \cup (P' \cap Q)$

5 The universal set $\mathcal{E} = \{\text{all integers from 5 to 20 inclusive}\}$.

If $A = \{\text{even numbers}\}$, $B = \{\text{multiples of 3}\}$, list the members of the following sets:

(a) A (b) B (c) $A \cap B$ (d) $A' \cap B$ (e) $(A \cup B)'$

6 A, B and C are subsets of the universal set:

$$\mathcal{E} = \{4,5,6,7,8,9,10,11,12,13\}$$
$$A = \{\text{even numbers}\}$$
$$B = \{\text{prime numbers}\}$$
$$C = \{\text{multiples of 4}\}$$

Copy the given Venn diagram and write each of the elements in its correct region.

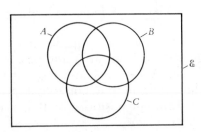

7   If $\mathscr{E} = \{0, 3\frac{1}{3}, -\frac{11}{3}, \sqrt{10}, -5\}$ write down:
    (a) the largest element of $\mathscr{E}$,   (b) the smallest element of $\mathscr{E}$.

8   If $\mathscr{E} = \{\sin 30°, \cos 30°, \tan 30°\}$ write down:
    (a) the largest element in $\mathscr{E}$,   (b) the smallest element in $\mathscr{E}$.

9   If $\mathscr{E} = \{8^{\frac{2}{3}}, 8^0, (\frac{1}{2})^{-3}\}$ write down:
    (a) the largest element of $\mathscr{E}$,   (b) the smallest element of $\mathscr{E}$.

10 Draw diagrams to illustrate each of the following:
    (a) $A \cap B$ (b) $A \cap B = \emptyset$ (c) $A \subset B$ (d) $A \subset B \subset C$

11 If $\mathscr{E} = \{x : x \in 1, 2, 3, 4, 5, 6, 7, 8\}$ write down all possible x satisfying:
    (a) $x + 2 < 7$ (b) $2x + 3 < 19$
    (c) $x - 3 > 2$ (d) $(x - 2)(x - 7) > 0$

12 If $\mathscr{E} = \{x : x \in 5, 6, 7, 8, 9, 10, 11, 12\}$ write down all possible x satisfying:
    (a) $x - 4 > 6$ (b) $x + 2 < 10$
    (c) $2x - 5 < 11$ (d) $(x - 5)(x - 9) > 0$

13 If $\mathscr{E} = \{people\}$, $X = \{mathematicians\}$, $Y = \{women\}$, show these in a Venn diagram and shade the region which illustrates that some women are not mathematicians.

14 Show in a Venn diagram the relation between the sets:

$$\mathscr{E} = \{natural\ numbers\}$$
$$X = \{multiples\ of\ 2\}$$
$$Y = \{multiples\ of\ 3\}$$

Describe the elements of the sets:
    (a) $X \cap Y$ (b) $X \cup Y$ (c) $X \cap Y'$

15 If $\mathscr{E} = \{triangles\}$, $X = \{triangles\ containing\ a\ right\ angle\}$, $Y = \{isosceles\ triangles\}$, $Z = \{equiangular\ triangles\}$, draw a Venn diagram to show the relationship between them.

Describe the elements of:
    (a) $X \cap Y$ (b) $X' \cap Y$ (c) $X' \cap Y'$

List the elements in $X \cap Z$.

16 If $\mathscr{E} = \{quadrilaterals\}$, $A = \{parallelograms\}$, $B = \{rectangles\}$ and $C = \{squares\}$, draw a Venn diagram to illustrate the connection between the sets.

17 In a group of 33 pupils, 26 passed an English test, 21 passed a Maths test and three passed neither. How many passed in both subjects?

99

18 Show in a Venn diagram the relationship between the sets
    & = {positive integers less than 15}, X = {multiples of 2},
    Y = {multiples of 3}. List the elements of:

(a) X ∩ Y   (b) X ∪ Y   (c) X ∩ Y'   (d) X' ∩ Y

State $n(X \cup Y)'$.

19 Given:

$$\text{\&} = \{\text{letters of the alphabet}\}$$
$$A = \{b, u, y, a\}$$
$$B = \{m, o, d, e, r, n\}$$
$$C = \{c, o, m, p, u, t, e, r\}$$

Write down:

(a) the elements in the set $(A \cup B) \cap C$,

(b) $n(A \cap B)$.

20 If there are 70 elements in the universal set & and A and B are
    subsets of & such that $n(A) = 40$, $n(B) = 25$ and $n(A \cup B)' = 14$
    use a Venn diagram to find $n(A \cap B)$.

21 If there are 32 elements in the universal set & and A and B are
    subsets of & such that $n(A) = 17$, $n(B) = 13$ and $n(A \cap B) = 3$,
    use a Venn diagram to find $n(A \cup B)'$.

22 In the accompanying Venn diagram the 4 in the shaded area means
    that $n(A \cap B) = 4$, i.e. there are four elements in the set $A \cap B$.
    Use the numbers in the other regions to find:

(a) $n(A)$ (b) $n(B)$ (c) $n(A \cup B)$
(d) $n(A')$ (e) $n(B')$ (f) $n(A' \cup B)$
(g) $n(A \cup B')$ (h) $n(A' \cap B')$ (i) $n(A' \cap B)$
(j) $n(A \cap B)'$

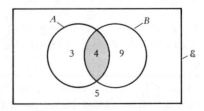

100

23 Draw a Venn diagram to show three sets A, B and C which are subsets of the universal set ε. Use the following information to fill in the number of elements in each region: $n(A \cap B \cap C) = 3$, $n(A \cap B) = 6$, $n(A \cap C) = 8$, $n(B \cap C) = 5$, $n(A) = 14$, $n(B) = 18$, $n(C) = 14$, $n(\varepsilon) = 40$. Find:

(a) $n(A' \cap B' \cap C')$ (b) $n(A \cap B' \cap C')$

24 The universal set $\varepsilon = \{$positive integers from 1 to 30 inclusive$\}$. X, Y and Z are subsets of ε and are defined as follows:

$$X = \{\text{multiples of } 4\}$$
$$Y = \{\text{multiples of } 5\}$$
$$Z = \{\text{prime numbers}\}$$

List the elements of the sets:

(a) $X \cup Y$ (b) $X \cap Z$

(c) $(X \cap Y \cap Z)'$ (d) $(X \cup Y) \cap (Y \cup Z)$

25 In Perfectland all the people belong to one or more of the three groups Blinks (X), Blonks (Y) and Blunks (Z) as indicated in the Venn diagram.

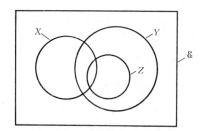

Which of the following statements are true?

(a) All Blunks are Blonks.

(b) All Blonks are Blinks.

(c) Some Blinks are Blunks.

(d) If a person is a Blunk he cannot be a Blink.

(e) Some Blonks are Blinks but not Blunks.

101

26   The given Venn diagram shows the number of players at a Sports' Club who take part in various sporting activities.

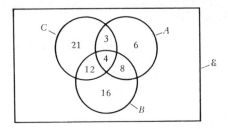

$$A = \{\text{members who take part in archery}\}$$
$$B = \{\text{members who play badminton}\}$$
$$C = \{\text{members who play cricket}\}$$

Find the number who:

(a) play cricket,

(b) take part in more than one activity,

(c) play badminton but not cricket,

(d) do not take part in archery.

27   Every pupil on a school trip to see Macbeth sat GCSE examinations in English (E), Mathematics (M) and a Science (S). Everyone passed in at least one subject, ten passed in all three subjects, four passed in English and Maths but not a Science, sixteen passed in Maths and a Science, eighteen passed in English and a Science, twenty-six passed Maths, two more passed English than Maths, and one pupil passed in a Science but in nothing else.

How many pupils sat GCSEs?

How many passed in two or more subjects?

28   Eighty-five boys in the third year had to choose their subjects for the fourth year. Their choices included the following: Woodwork 40, Metalwork 31, Technical Drawing 49, Woodwork and Metalwork 22, Woodwork and Technical Drawing 36, Metalwork and Technical Drawing 26. If x boys decided to study all three and 27 opted out completely, form an equation in x and solve it. Hence find how many boys were:

(a) not studying metalwork,

(b) studying exactly two of the three subjects,

(c) studying metalwork only.

29 A coach party of 51 passengers consists of x married couples plus their children. There are 5 more boys than men, and 2 more girls than women. Copy the Venn diagram and shade the region(s) which must be empty. (M = males, F = females and A = adults.)

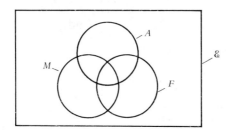

Form an equation in x and solve it. Hence determine:
(a) the number of females in the party,
(b) the number of children in the party.

30 A dental surgeon sees 38 patients in a day for one or more of the following reasons: an inspection (I), fillings (F), an extraction (E). He inspects 23 patients, does fillings for 18 and performs extractions for 8. If one more patient has an inspection and fillings than has an inspection and extraction, and no patient has fillings and an extraction, find the number of patients:
(a) having an extraction only,
(b) having both an inspection and fillings.

Determinants and Matrices 26

Find the following determinants:

$$1 \quad \begin{vmatrix} 4 & 3 \\ 2 & 5 \end{vmatrix} \qquad 2 \quad \begin{vmatrix} 5 & 9 \\ 2 & 7 \end{vmatrix} \qquad 3 \quad \begin{vmatrix} -3 & 5 \\ 5 & 4 \end{vmatrix}$$

$$4 \quad \begin{vmatrix} 14 & 3 \\ 9 & 2 \end{vmatrix} \qquad 5 \quad \begin{vmatrix} 6 & 12 \\ 3 & 6 \end{vmatrix} \qquad 6 \quad \begin{vmatrix} -7 & 5 \\ 5 & -4 \end{vmatrix}$$

$$7 \quad \begin{vmatrix} 113 & 56 \\ 5 & 2 \end{vmatrix} \qquad 8 \quad \begin{vmatrix} -9 & 15 \\ 7 & -8 \end{vmatrix} \qquad 9 \quad \begin{vmatrix} 46 & 13 \\ 12 & 13 \end{vmatrix}$$

$$10 \quad \begin{vmatrix} -15 & -7 \\ 14 & -9 \end{vmatrix} \qquad 11 \quad \begin{vmatrix} 23 & 0 \\ 15 & -1 \end{vmatrix} \qquad 12 \quad \begin{vmatrix} -16 & 7 \\ -1 & 0 \end{vmatrix}$$

13   If $A = \begin{pmatrix} 4 & 3 \\ 3 & 2 \end{pmatrix}$ and $B = \begin{pmatrix} 5 & 2 \\ 3 & 2 \end{pmatrix}$ find:

    (a) $A + B$ (b) $2A - B$ (c) $3A - I$

    (d) AB (e) BA (f) A^2

14   If $X \begin{pmatrix} -5 & 4 \\ 2 & 6 \end{pmatrix}$ and $Y = \begin{pmatrix} 7 & -3 \\ 8 & 2 \end{pmatrix}$ find:

    (a) $3X + 2Y$ (b) $4X - Y$ (c) X^2 (d) XY

15   If $A \begin{pmatrix} 9 & 4 \\ 7 & 5 \end{pmatrix}$ and $B = \begin{pmatrix} 8 & 3 \\ 5 & 2 \end{pmatrix}$ find:

    (a) $A + 2B$ (b) $3A + 2B$ (c) $3B - A$

    (d) BA (e) AB (f) B^2

16   If $A = \begin{pmatrix} -4 & 7 \\ 5 & -4 \end{pmatrix}$ and $B = \begin{pmatrix} -9 & 5 \\ -2 & 6 \end{pmatrix}$ find:

    (a) $4A$ (b) $2B$ (c) $B + 2A$

    (d) $B - I$ (e) BA (f) B^2

17   If $X = \begin{pmatrix} 12 & -3 \\ 0 & 7 \end{pmatrix}$ and $Y = \begin{pmatrix} -9 & 15 \\ 3 & -4 \end{pmatrix}$ find:

    (a) $X + 3Y$ (b) $X - Y$ (c) $I - Y$

    (d) XY (e) X^2 (f) X^3

18   If $A = \begin{pmatrix} 5 & 6 \\ 6 & 7 \end{pmatrix}$ find A^{-1} and use this value to find AA^{-1} and $A^{-1}A$.

19   If $X = \begin{pmatrix} 9 & 5 \\ 8 & 5 \end{pmatrix}$ find X^{-1} and use this value to find XX^{-1} and $X^{-1}X$.

20   If $M = \begin{pmatrix} -4 & -5 \\ 2 & 3 \end{pmatrix}$ find M^{-1} and hence find the value of MM^{-1} and $M^{-1}M$.

21   If $Y = \begin{pmatrix} 16 & 6 \\ 3 & 3 \end{pmatrix}$ find Y^{-1} and the value of YY^{-1}.

22   If $Z = \begin{pmatrix} 5 & 6 \\ 3 & -4 \end{pmatrix}$ find Z^{-1} and ZZ^{-1}.

23   If $A = \begin{pmatrix} 7 & 2 \\ 5 & 3 \end{pmatrix}$ and $B = \begin{pmatrix} 6 \\ 3 \end{pmatrix}$ find AB.

24   If $X = \begin{pmatrix} -6 & 4 \\ 4 & 5 \end{pmatrix}$ and $Y = \begin{pmatrix} -8 \\ 3 \end{pmatrix}$ find XY.

25   If $C = \begin{pmatrix} 9 & 13 \\ 7 & -4 \end{pmatrix}$ and $D = \begin{pmatrix} 13 \\ -8 \end{pmatrix}$ find CD.

Transformations

1 Find the image of the point $P(5,3)$ under the transformation T, given by the matrix $\begin{pmatrix} 0 & 1 \\ -1 & 2 \end{pmatrix}$.

2 Find the image of the point $A(-4,2)$ under the transformation S, given by the matrix $\begin{pmatrix} -2 & 0 \\ 0 & -2 \end{pmatrix}$.

If the image of a point B under the same transformation is $(-2,6)$ find the coordinates of B.

3 The transformation $M:\begin{pmatrix} x \\ y \end{pmatrix} \rightarrow \begin{pmatrix} x' \\ y' \end{pmatrix}$ is such that $x' = 2x - 4y$ and $y' = 3x + 5y$. Write down the matrix associated with M.

4 The transformation $N:\begin{pmatrix} x \\ y \end{pmatrix} \rightarrow \begin{pmatrix} x' \\ y' \end{pmatrix}$ is such that $2x' = 3x + 5y$ and $3y' = x - 4y$. Write down the matrix associated with N.

5 The transformation $T:\begin{pmatrix} x \\ y \end{pmatrix} \rightarrow \begin{pmatrix} 0 & -1 \\ 1 & 0 \end{pmatrix}\begin{pmatrix} x \\ y \end{pmatrix}$. Use this transformation to find:

(a) the images of the points $\begin{pmatrix} 5 \\ -4 \end{pmatrix}$ and $\begin{pmatrix} -3 \\ -4 \end{pmatrix}$,

(b) $\begin{pmatrix} x \\ y \end{pmatrix}$ which is mapped on to $\begin{pmatrix} -4 \\ 4 \end{pmatrix}$.

6 The transformation $T:\begin{pmatrix} x \\ y \end{pmatrix} \rightarrow \begin{pmatrix} -1 & 0 \\ 0 & 2 \end{pmatrix}\begin{pmatrix} x \\ y \end{pmatrix}$. Use this transformation to find:

(a) the images of the points $\begin{pmatrix} 5 \\ 2 \end{pmatrix}$ and $\begin{pmatrix} -5 \\ 4 \end{pmatrix}$,

(b) $\begin{pmatrix} x \\ y \end{pmatrix}$ which is mapped on to $\begin{pmatrix} 5 \\ 8 \end{pmatrix}$.

7 T is the transformation $\begin{pmatrix} x \\ y \end{pmatrix} \rightarrow \begin{pmatrix} 0 & 1 \\ -1 & 0 \end{pmatrix}\begin{pmatrix} x \\ y \end{pmatrix}$. Using this transformation:

(a) Write down the images of the points $\begin{pmatrix} -2 \\ 6 \end{pmatrix}$ and $\begin{pmatrix} 5 \\ -3 \end{pmatrix}$.

(b) Find $\begin{pmatrix} x \\ y \end{pmatrix}$ which is mapped on to $\begin{pmatrix} -3 \\ -4 \end{pmatrix}$.

8   Plot the points $O(0,0)$, $A(4,3)$ and $B(3,4)$ on squared paper. A transformation T is represented by the matrix $M = \begin{pmatrix} 2 & 0 \\ 0 & 2 \end{pmatrix}$. Use this transformation to find the images of O, A and B, denoting them by O, A′ and B′, and plotting them in your diagram.

Find the areas of triangles OAB and OA′B′. Hence determine the ratio $\dfrac{\triangle OA'B'}{\triangle OAB}$ and compare this value with the determinant of M.

9   M_1 and M_2 are transformations defined by the matrices $M_1 = \begin{pmatrix} 0 & -1 \\ 1 & 0 \end{pmatrix}$ and $M_2 = \begin{pmatrix} 1 & 2 \\ 0 & 1 \end{pmatrix}$. Determine the images of the vertices of the triangle $O(0,0)$, $A(4,3)$ and $B(2,6)$ when M_1M_2 is applied to them, illustrating your results on a diagram. Repeat the process for M_2M_1. Is the effect of M_1M_2 the same as that of M_2M_1?

Determine the area of triangle OAB. Is the area preserved under either (or both) of the above transformations?

10   The matrix $A = \begin{pmatrix} 4 & -2 \\ 3 & -3 \end{pmatrix}$ represents the transformation
$T: \begin{pmatrix} x \\ y \end{pmatrix} \rightarrow \begin{pmatrix} 4 & -2 \\ 3 & -3 \end{pmatrix} \begin{pmatrix} x \\ y \end{pmatrix}$. Find:
   (a) the coordinates of the points into which $(3,5)$ and $(-3,5)$ are mapped by the transformation T,
   (b) the inverse of A,
   (c) the coordinates of the point which is mapped to $(12,15)$ under the transformation T,
   (d) the matrix A^2,
   (e) the matrix B such that $A^2 - B = A$.

11   A transformation X is described by the matrix $\begin{pmatrix} 0 & -1 \\ -1 & 0 \end{pmatrix}$, and a translation Y is described by the vector $\begin{pmatrix} 3 \\ 3 \end{pmatrix}$.

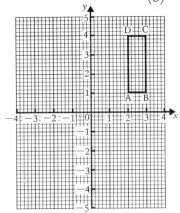

106

(a) Copy the diagram opposite, and show the image of the rectangle ABCD under the transformation X. Label the image A′B′C′D′. Describe this transformation in geometrical terms.

(b) Show the image of A′B′C′D′ under the translation Y. Label this image A″B″C″D″. Describe in geometrical terms the single transformation that maps ABCD on to A″B″C″D″.

12 The transformation M is described by the matrix $\begin{pmatrix} 0 & -1 \\ -1 & 0 \end{pmatrix}$. N is the translation described by the vector $\begin{pmatrix} 2 \\ 2 \end{pmatrix}$.

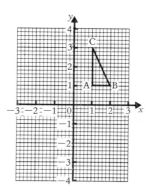

(a) Copy the diagram and show the image of triangle ABC under the transformation M. Mark the image $A_1B_1C_1$. Describe the transformation in geometrical terms.

(b) Show the image of triangle $A_1B_1C_1$ under the translation N. Mark the image $A_2B_2C_2$. Describe, in geometrical terms, the single transformation that will map ABC on to $A_2B_2C_2$.

13 The vertices of a triangle ABC have coordinates $A(-4,2)$, $B(4,3)$ and $C(8,6)$. Triangle ABC is mapped on to triangle A′B′C′ by the transformation represented by the matrix M where $M = \begin{pmatrix} 0.8 & 0.6 \\ -0.6 & 0.8 \end{pmatrix}$.

(a) Find the coordinates of A′, B′ and C′.

(b) Draw, and label, the triangles ABC and A′B′C′ on a graph. Use 1 cm to represent 1 unit on each axis.

(c) Describe the transformation represented by M.

14

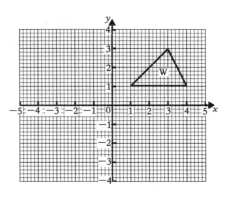

Copy the diagram given above.

(a) Draw the image of the triangle W after it has been rotated through half a turn about the origin. Label it X.

(b) Draw the image of the triangle W after the translation described by the vector $\begin{pmatrix} 0 \\ -4 \end{pmatrix}$. Label it Y.

(c) Draw the image of the triangle X after it has been rotated through a half-turn about the point $(0, -2)$. Label it Z.

(d) What do you notice about the triangles labelled Y and Z?

15

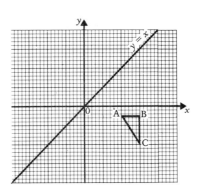

Copy the diagram given above.

(a) Draw the image of the triangle ABC after a rotation through one quarter of a turn anticlockwise about the origin. Label it $A_1B_1C_1$.

(b) Draw the image of $A_1B_1C_1$ when it is reflected in the line $y = x$. Label it $A_2B_2C_2$.

(c) Describe the single transformation that will transform ABC into $A_2B_2C_2$.

16

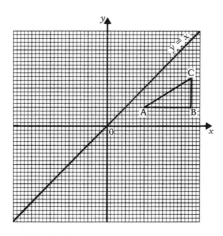

Copy the diagram given above.

(a) Draw the reflection of the triangle ABC in the line $y = x$, and label it $A_1B_1C_1$.

(b) Draw the reflection of $A_1B_1C_1$ in the y-axis and label it $A_2B_2C_2$.

(c) Describe the single transformation that will transform ABC into $A_2B_2C_2$.

(d) Draw the reflection of $A_1B_1C_1$ in the x-axis and label it $A_3B_3C_3$.

(e) Describe the single transformation that will transform ABC into $A_3B_3C_3$.

17

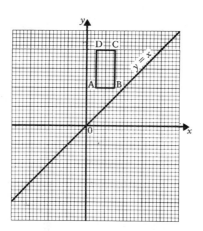

Copy the diagram given above.

(a) Draw the reflection of the rectangle ABCD in the line $y = x$ and label it $A_1B_1C_1D_1$.

(b) Draw the reflection of the rectangle $A_1B_1C_1D_1$ in the y-axis, and label it $A_2B_2C_2D_2$.

(c) Describe the single transformation that will transform ABCD into $A_2B_2C_2D_2$.

18

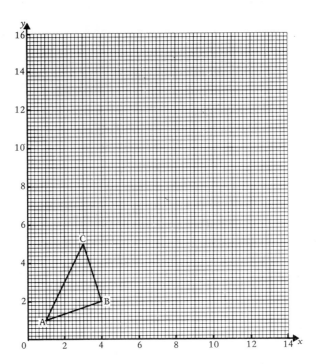

The grid shows a triangle ABC. Write down the coordinates of the vertices of this triangle.

B′(12,6) is the image of B under an enlargement with centre (0,0). Copy the diagram and on it mark the images A′ and C′ of A and C under the same enlargement.

What is the scale factor of the enlargement?

19

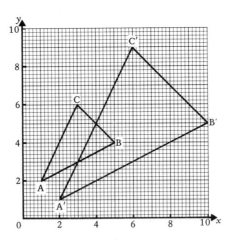

The graph shows the image A′B′C′ of a triangle ABC under an enlargement, centred at the point (a, b). Find the coordinates of the centre of enlargement and the scale factor of the enlargement.

20

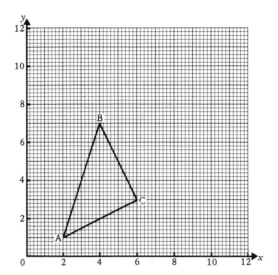

The grid shows a triangle ABC. Write down the coordinates of its vertices.

The image of A under a translation is the point A′ with coordinates $(8, 3)$. Mark A′ on your diagram and mark B′ and C′, the images of B and C, under the same translation. Write the vector, in the form $\begin{pmatrix} a \\ b \end{pmatrix}$, that describes this translation.

21 The transformation T consists of a reflection in the x-axis followed by an enlargement with centre $(0,0)$ and scale factor 2. Find:

(a) the images of $\begin{pmatrix} 1 \\ 0 \end{pmatrix}$ and $\begin{pmatrix} 0 \\ 2 \end{pmatrix}$ under T,

(b) the matrix associated with T,

(c) the images of $\begin{pmatrix} 3 \\ 2 \end{pmatrix}$ and $\begin{pmatrix} -2 \\ -3 \end{pmatrix}$ under T.

22 The transformation T consists of a reflection in the y-axis followed by an enlargement with centre $(0,0)$ and scale factor 3. Find:

(a) the images of $\begin{pmatrix} 1 \\ 0 \end{pmatrix}$ and $\begin{pmatrix} 0 \\ 1 \end{pmatrix}$ under T,

(b) the matrix associated with T,

(c) the images of $\begin{pmatrix} 3 \\ 2 \end{pmatrix}$ and $\begin{pmatrix} 2 \\ -3 \end{pmatrix}$ under T.

23 The transformation M consists of a reflection in the x-axis followed by a reflection in the y-axis. Find:

(a) the images of $\begin{pmatrix} 1 \\ 2 \end{pmatrix}$ and $\begin{pmatrix} 3 \\ 4 \end{pmatrix}$ under M,

(b) the matrix associated with M.

Vectors

1

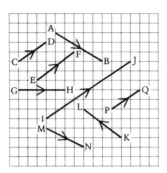

The diagram shows eight vectors on a unit grid.
(a) Write down two equal vectors.
(b) Write down two (or more) vectors that are equal in magnitude but not in direction.
(c) Which two unequal vectors are parallel. How are they related?

2 If $a = \begin{pmatrix} 4 \\ -2 \end{pmatrix}$ draw diagrams to represent:

(a) a   (b) 2a   (c) $\frac{1}{2}$a   (d) −a   (e) −2a   (f) 3a

3 If $a = \begin{pmatrix} 3 \\ 2 \end{pmatrix}$ and $b = \begin{pmatrix} -5 \\ 3 \end{pmatrix}$ draw diagrams to represent:

(a) a   (b) b   (c) a + b   (d) a − b

4 If A, B and C are the points $(2, -3)$, $(-2, 4)$ and $(3, 2)$ respectively write down the vectors $\overrightarrow{AB}$, $\overrightarrow{BC}$ and $\overrightarrow{CA}$.

5 If X, Y and Z are the points $(-1, -4)$, $(2, 5)$ and $(6, -3)$ respectively write down the vectors $\overrightarrow{XY}$, $\overrightarrow{ZY}$ and $\overrightarrow{ZX}$.

6 If A, B and C are the points $(1, 1)$, $(5, 6)$ and $(7, 3)$ respectively write down the vectors $\overrightarrow{CB}$, $\overrightarrow{AB}$ and $\overrightarrow{AC}$.

7 Which of the vectors given below is:

(a) parallel to,   (b) perpendicular to, the vector $\begin{pmatrix} -3 \\ 2 \end{pmatrix}$?

$$\begin{pmatrix} -3 \\ -2 \end{pmatrix} \quad \begin{pmatrix} 6 \\ 4 \end{pmatrix} \quad \begin{pmatrix} -6 \\ 4 \end{pmatrix} \quad \begin{pmatrix} 12 \\ -8 \end{pmatrix} \quad \begin{pmatrix} 3 \\ -2 \end{pmatrix} \quad \begin{pmatrix} 2 \\ 3 \end{pmatrix} \quad \begin{pmatrix} 2 \\ -3 \end{pmatrix}$$

8   Which of the following vectors is:

(a) parallel to,   (b) perpendicular to, the vector $\begin{pmatrix} 3 \\ -1 \end{pmatrix}$?

$$\begin{pmatrix} 3 \\ 1 \end{pmatrix} \quad \begin{pmatrix} 1 \\ 3 \end{pmatrix} \quad \begin{pmatrix} 6 \\ -2 \end{pmatrix} \quad \begin{pmatrix} 2 \\ -6 \end{pmatrix} \quad \begin{pmatrix} -1 \\ -3 \end{pmatrix} \quad \begin{pmatrix} -3 \\ 1 \end{pmatrix}$$

9   A is the point $(-2, -2)$, $\overrightarrow{AB} = \begin{pmatrix} 7 \\ -2 \end{pmatrix}$ and $\overrightarrow{AC} = \begin{pmatrix} 0 \\ 8 \end{pmatrix}$.

(a) Find the coordinates of B and C.

(b) Find the gradient of BC and the vector $\overrightarrow{CB}$.

10   ABC is a triangle such that A is the point $(-4, -2)$, $\overrightarrow{AB} = \begin{pmatrix} 6 \\ 6 \end{pmatrix}$ and $\overrightarrow{AC} = \begin{pmatrix} 8 \\ -2 \end{pmatrix}$. Find:

(a) the coordinates of B and C,

(b) the vector $\overrightarrow{CB}$,

(c) the coordinates of M, the midpoint of BC.

11   P, Q, R and S are four points such that P is $(-6, 4)$, R is $(6, 2)$, $\overrightarrow{PQ} = \begin{pmatrix} 8 \\ 2 \end{pmatrix}$ and $\overrightarrow{PS} = \begin{pmatrix} 8 \\ -8 \end{pmatrix}$. Calculate:

(a) the coordinates of Q and S,

(b) the vectors $\overrightarrow{QR}$ and $\overrightarrow{RS}$.

What can you conclude about the quadrilateral PQRS?

12   A, B, C and D are four points such that C is $(-2, -4)$, $\overrightarrow{CD} = \begin{pmatrix} -2 \\ 6 \end{pmatrix}$, $\overrightarrow{CA} = \begin{pmatrix} 4 \\ 8 \end{pmatrix}$ and $\overrightarrow{CB} = \begin{pmatrix} 6 \\ 2 \end{pmatrix}$. Find the coordinates of A, B and D.

13   ABC is an isosceles triangle with $\angle BAC = 90°$ and $AB = AC$. If A is the point $(2, 3)$, C is the point $(6, -4)$ and B is the point $(x, -1)$ find:

(a) the vector $\overrightarrow{AC}$,

(b) the value of x,

(c) the vector $\overrightarrow{BC}$.

113

14 a, b and c are vectors such that:

$$a = \begin{pmatrix} 2 \\ 3 \end{pmatrix} \qquad b = \begin{pmatrix} -2 \\ 4 \end{pmatrix} \qquad c = \begin{pmatrix} 16 \\ 3 \end{pmatrix}$$

Find vectors x and y such that:

(a) a + x = b

(b) 2y − 3b = 2c

Find scalars r and s which satisfy ra + sb = c.

15 a, b and c are vectors such that:

$$a = \begin{pmatrix} 2 \\ 1 \end{pmatrix} \qquad b = \begin{pmatrix} 3 \\ -2 \end{pmatrix} \qquad c = \begin{pmatrix} -3 \\ 2 \end{pmatrix}$$

Find:

(a) a + b + c

(b) 2a − b + 3c

(c) x if x + a − b = 3c

16 Vectors a, b and c are such that:

$$a = \begin{pmatrix} 2 \\ 3 \end{pmatrix} \qquad b = \begin{pmatrix} -1 \\ 2 \end{pmatrix} \qquad c = \begin{pmatrix} 4 \\ -2 \end{pmatrix}$$

Find:

(a) a + 2b + 3c

(b) 3c − b + 2a

(c) x if 2x + c = a − 4b

17

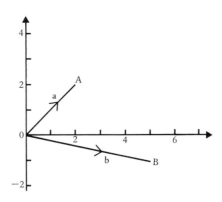

In the diagram $\overrightarrow{OA}$ = a and $\overrightarrow{OB}$ = b.

(a) From the point O draw the vector $\overrightarrow{OC}$ such that $\overrightarrow{OC}$ = a + b.

(b) Find $\overrightarrow{AB}$ in terms of a and b.

(c) Give the components of $\overrightarrow{AB}$.

18 Quadrilateral ABCD is such that B is $(2,5)$, C is $(8,2)$, D is $(2,0)$ and $\overrightarrow{AD} = \begin{pmatrix} 4 \\ -2 \end{pmatrix}$. Calculate:

(a) the vector $\overrightarrow{BC}$,

(b) the coordinates of A,

(c) the geometrical relationship between AD and BC.

19 In a triangle OAB, $\overrightarrow{OA} = \mathbf{a}$ and $\overrightarrow{OB} = \mathbf{b}$. E is a point on AB such that $AE:EB = 2:1$. Find, in terms of $\mathbf{a}$ and $\mathbf{b}$:

(a) $\overrightarrow{AB}$ (b) $\overrightarrow{AE}$ (c) $\overrightarrow{OE}$

20

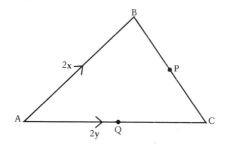

In the triangle ABC, P and Q are the midpoints of BC and AC respectively. $AB = 2x$ and $AC = 2y$.

(a) (i) Find $\overrightarrow{CB}$, $\overrightarrow{CP}$ and $\overrightarrow{AP}$ in terms of x and y.

(ii) If G is a point on AP such that $AG = \frac{2}{3}AP$ find $\overrightarrow{AG}$ in terms of x and y.

(b) (i) Find BQ in terms of x and y.

(ii) If H is a point on BQ such that $BH = \frac{2}{3}BQ$ find $\overrightarrow{HB}$ in terms of x and y. Hence find $\overrightarrow{AH}$ in terms of x and y. What conclusion may be drawn about the points G and H?

21

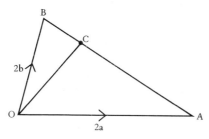

C is the point on the side AB of a triangle OAB that divides AB in the ratio $3:1$. Given that $\overrightarrow{OA} = 2\mathbf{a}$ and $\overrightarrow{OB} = 2\mathbf{b}$, find, in terms of $\mathbf{a}$ and $\mathbf{b}$, expressions for:

(a) $\overrightarrow{AB}$ (b) $\overrightarrow{CB}$ (c) $\overrightarrow{OC}$

22

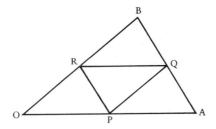

P, Q and R are the midpoints respectively of the sides OA, AB and OB of a triangle OAB. Given that $\overrightarrow{OA} = 2a$, and $\overrightarrow{OB} = 2b$, find, in terms of a and b, expressions for:

(a) $\overrightarrow{AB}$ (b) $\overrightarrow{OP}$ (c) $\overrightarrow{OR}$ (d) $\overrightarrow{PR}$

Write down the geometrical relationship between PR and AB.

23

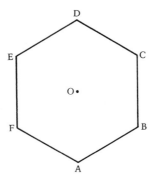

ABCDEF is a regular hexagon with O as centre. The vectors p and q are such that $\overrightarrow{AB} = p$ and $\overrightarrow{BC} = q$. Express each of the following vectors in terms of p and q.

(a) $\overrightarrow{AC}$ (b) $\overrightarrow{AD}$ (c) $\overrightarrow{CD}$ (d) $\overrightarrow{FA}$ (e) $\overrightarrow{FB}$

24

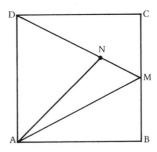

ABCD is a square. M is the midpoint of BC and N is the point on MD that divides it in the ratio $1:2$. The vectors $2x$ and $2y$ are such that $\overrightarrow{AB} = 2x$ and $\overrightarrow{AD} = 2y$. Express each of the following vectors in terms of x and y.

(a) $\overrightarrow{BM}$ (b) $\overrightarrow{AM}$ (c) $\overrightarrow{MD}$ (d) $\overrightarrow{ND}$ (e) $\overrightarrow{AN}$ (f) $\overrightarrow{AC}$

What can you deduce about N and the line AC?

25

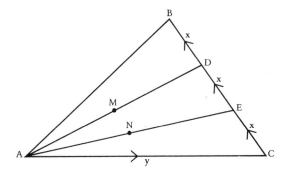

ABC is a triangle with D and E points on BC such that
$\overrightarrow{CE} = \overrightarrow{ED} = \overrightarrow{DB} = x$ and $\overrightarrow{AC} = y$.

(a) Find $\overrightarrow{AE}$ and $\overrightarrow{AD}$ in terms of x and y.

(b) If M and N are the midpoints of AD and AE respectively find $\overrightarrow{AM}$ and $\overrightarrow{AN}$ in terms of x and y.

(c) Find $\overrightarrow{NM}$ in terms of x and y.

(d) What conclusion can you draw about NM and CB?

26

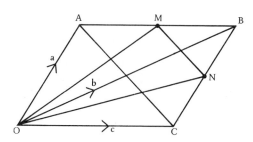

OABC is a parallelogram with M and N the midpoints of AB and BC respectively. $\overrightarrow{OA} = a$, $\overrightarrow{OB} = b$ and $\overrightarrow{OC} = c$.

(a) Find $\overrightarrow{AB}$ and $\overrightarrow{CB}$ in terms of a and c.

(b) Find $\overrightarrow{OM}$ and $\overrightarrow{ON}$ in terms of a and c.

(c) Find $\overrightarrow{MN}$ and $\overrightarrow{AC}$ in terms of a and b.

(d) What can you conclude about MN and AC?

27 From an origin O, three points A, B and C are such that $\overrightarrow{OA} = a$, $\overrightarrow{OB} = b$ and $\overrightarrow{OC} = c$. If M is the midpoint of AC and if G is the point on BM such that BG:GM = 2:1 find, in terms of a, b and c:

(a) $\overrightarrow{AC}$ and $\overrightarrow{AM}$ (b) $\overrightarrow{OM}$ and $\overrightarrow{MB}$ (c) $\overrightarrow{MG}$ and $\overrightarrow{OG}$

28 In triangle OAC, M is the midpoint of OA and B is the midpoint of OC. Given that $\overrightarrow{OA} = 2a$ and $\overrightarrow{OB} = b$, express the vectors $\overrightarrow{OM}$, $\overrightarrow{OC}$, $\overrightarrow{AC}$ and $\overrightarrow{MB}$ in terms of a and b. Hence prove that MB is parallel to AC.

State the ratio of the area of triangle OMB to the area of triangle OAC.

29 The diagram, which is drawn on a unit grid, shows part of a 'crazy' golf course, the shaded areas representing obstructions. A golf ball struck against any side rebounds at the same angle as it strikes it.

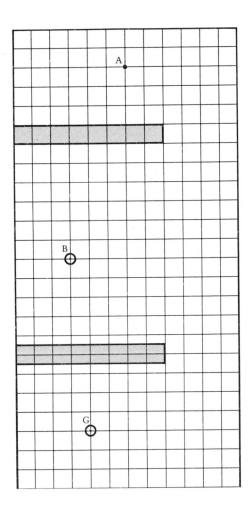

(a) Tom stands with the ball at A and strikes it towards a point C so that it rebounds and falls into the hole B. Express the vectors $\overrightarrow{AC}$ and $\overrightarrow{CB}$ as column vectors.

(b) Prunella, his partner, places a ball at A and attempts to strike it in a similar way. It misses the hole B but, after three rebounds at D, E and F, falls into the hole at G. Express the vectors $\overrightarrow{AD}$, $\overrightarrow{DE}$, $\overrightarrow{EF}$ as column vectors.

(c) Write down the column vectors for $\overrightarrow{AB}$ and $\overrightarrow{BG}$, if the obstructions were removed.

Functions 29

1 A function f is defined by $f(x) = x^2 - 11x + 18$.
   (a) Find (i) $f(3)$ (ii) $f(-3)$.
   (b) Find the values of x for which:
      (i) $f(x) = 0$ (ii) $f(x) = 18$

2 A function f is defined by $f(x) = 2x - 1$. Write down the values of:
   (a) $f(2)$ (b) $f(-3)$ (c) x if $f(x) = 9$
   (d) $f(2x)$ (e) $f(f(x))$

3 A function f is defined by $f(x) = 5x + 2$ and a function g is defined by $g(x) = x^2$. Find:
   (a) $f(3)$ (b) $g(-3)$ (c) $f(g(-3))$
   (d) $g(f(3))$ (e) x if $f(x) = -13$

4 If f is defined by $f(x) = 3x + 1$ and g is defined by $g(x) = 5 - 2x$, find:
   (a) $f(4)$ (b) $g(5)$ (c) $f[g(5)]$
   (d) x if $g(x) = 13$
   Show also that $f(x + y) = f(x) + f(y) - 1$.

5 Given that $f(x) = 9^x$, find:
   (a) $f(\frac{3}{2})$ (b) $f(-\frac{1}{2})$ (c) $f(0)$

6 A function f is defined by $f(x) = x^2 + 4x - 12$.
   (a) Find:
      (i) $f(3)$ (ii) $f(-3)$ (iii) $f(0)$
   (b) Find the values of x for which:
      (i) $f(x) = 0$ (ii) $f(x) = -12$ (iii) $f(x) = -16$

7 Given that $f(x) = 2^x$ find:
   (a) $f(4)$ (b) $f(-2)$ (c) x if $f(x) = \dfrac{\sqrt{2}}{2}$

The Sine Rule and Cosine Rule   30

1 Evaluate:

(a) $\dfrac{14 \sin 42°}{\sin 74°}$

(b) $\dfrac{27 \sin 56°}{\sin 37°}$

(c) $\dfrac{5.8 \sin 79°}{\sin 48°}$

(d) $\dfrac{3.97 \sin 62.1°}{\sin 47.6°}$

(e) $\dfrac{9.73 \sin 29°}{\sin 82°}$

(f) $\dfrac{120 \sin 35°}{\sin 65°}$

(g) $\dfrac{8.26 \sin 74.2°}{\sin 50.9°}$

(h) $\dfrac{17.4 \sin 51.8°}{\sin 64.3°}$

(i) $\dfrac{32.7 \sin 73°}{\sin 27°}$

2 Find the acute angle A correct to the nearest tenth of a degree if:

(a) $\sin A = \dfrac{12 \sin 42°}{14}$

(b) $\sin A = \dfrac{9.23 \sin 59°}{12.4}$

(c) $\sin A = \dfrac{82 \sin 64.2°}{104}$

(d) $\sin A = \dfrac{3.42 \sin 73.7°}{3.51}$

(e) $\sin A = \dfrac{36 \sin 57°}{58}$

(f) $\sin A = \dfrac{53 \sin 41°}{73}$

(g) $\sin A = \dfrac{28 \sin 44.5°}{19.8}$

(h) $\sin A = \dfrac{8.92 \sin 36.4°}{13.64}$

3 In the questions that follow find the unknown sides and angles. Give sides correct to three significant figures and angles correct to the nearest tenth of a degree.

(a) $\dfrac{a}{\sin 50°} = \dfrac{14}{\sin 70°} = \dfrac{c}{\sin C}$

(b) $\dfrac{34}{\sin 74°} = \dfrac{b}{\sin 50°} = \dfrac{c}{\sin C}$

(c) $\dfrac{a}{\sin 84.2°} = \dfrac{b}{\sin B} = \dfrac{12}{\sin 48.8°}$

(d) $\dfrac{6.24}{\sin 38.6°} = \dfrac{b}{\sin 63.7°} = \dfrac{c}{\sin C}$

4 The bearings of a tree from two points A and B, 200 metres apart on a straight path running north-east, are S56°E and S22°W respectively. Find the distance of the tree from each observation point.

5 At noon a ship is 10 nautical miles north-east of a lighthouse, and is steaming on a course N42°W. At 12.30 p.m. the direction of the ship from the lighthouse is N16°E. Find the distance travelled by the ship between noon and 12.30 p.m. Hence calculate the speed of the ship.

6 Two villages, A and B, are 3.4 km apart. They lie on a straight road and the bearing from A to B is 298°. If the bearings of an electricity pylon, C, from A and B are respectively 214° and 154°, calculate the distance of the pylon from each village.

7   A batsman strikes a ball from A directly towards a fielder F in a direction making an angle 36° with the line of the wickets. The fielder picks up the ball and throws it, at an angle of 52° with the line of the wickets, to the other wicket B. If the distance between A and B is 20 metres, how far is the fielder from (a) A (b) B?

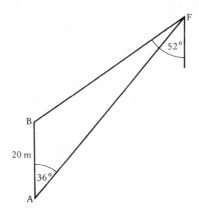

8   P and Q are two coastguard stations 10 km apart, P being in a direction N40°W of Q. A yacht (Y) sends out a distress signal which is received by both stations. If the directions of the signals indicate that Y is N74°E of P and N33°E of Q, find the distance of the yacht from each station.

9   Three farms A, B and C are such that A is one kilometre in a direction S76°E from B, the direction of C from B is N38°E, and the direction of A from C is S63°E. Find the distance of C from each of the other two farms.

10   Evaluate:
   (a) $2 \times 12 \times 36 \cos 67°$ (b) $2 \times 43 \times 23 \cos 74°$
   (c) $2 \times 5.2 \times 6.3 \cos 49°$ (d) $2 \times 8.5 \times 7.6 \cos 56°$

11   Find a if:
   (a) $a^2 = 4^2 + 5^2 - 2 \times 4 \times 5 \cos 60°$
   (b) $a^2 = 12^2 + 16^2 - 2 \times 12 \times 16 \cos 45°$
   (c) $a^2 = 4.2^2 + 5.8^2 - 2 \times 4.2 \times 5.8 \cos 57°$
   (d) $a^2 = 9.3^2 + 7.6^2 - 2 \times 9.3 \times 7.6 \cos 37.3°$

12   Find angle A if:
   (a) $\cos A = \dfrac{4^2 + 5^2 - 6^2}{2 \times 4 \times 5}$ (b) $\cos A = \dfrac{12^2 + 10^2 - 9^2}{2 \times 12 \times 10}$
   (c) $\cos A = \dfrac{16^2 + 19^2 - 23^2}{2 \times 16 \times 19}$ (d) $\cos A = \dfrac{8^2 + 5^2 - 6^2}{2 \times 8 \times 5}$

13 ABC is a triangle in which $a = 8$ cm, $b = 10$ cm and $c = 14$ cm. Which is the largest angle? Find it, giving your answer correct to the nearest tenth of a degree.

14 The first hole at a certain golf course is 260 metres long. A golfer hits her drive the exact distance but when she arrives at her ball she finds that she is still 22 metres from the hole. Assuming that the ball travelled in a straight line, find the angle which her drive made with the direction of the hole.

15 Find the angle between the hands of a clock at 12.30. If the hour hand is 6 cm long and the minute hand is 8 cm long, how far apart are the tips of the hands at this time?

16 From Southampton, Cardiff is 145 km in a direction N59°W, and Norwich is 265 km in a direction N43°E. Find the distance and direction of Norwich from Cardiff.

17 Three direct railway lines connect the American cities of New York, Washington and Pittsburgh. From New York, Pittsburgh is 340 miles in a direction S87°W and Washington is 220 miles in a direction S49°W. Find the distance and direction of Pittsburgh from Washington. Find the area of land enclosed by the triangle with the three cities as vertices.

18 In a factory complex the main office is 270 metres from the main entrance in a direction N52°W, and the canteen is 130 metres in a direction S61°W. Find the distance and direction of the office from the canteen.

19

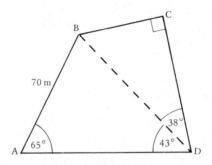

The diagram shows a field in the form of a quadrilateral ABCD

$$AB = 70 \text{ metres}, \quad B\widehat{A}D = 65°, \quad A\widehat{D}B = 43°,$$
$$B\widehat{D}C = 38° \quad \text{and} \quad B\widehat{C}D = 90°.$$

Find the lengths of the other three sides of the quadrilateral and the area of the field.

20 Two buoys A and B are 300 metres apart, B being north-east of A. From its mooring M the captain of a ship observes that the direction of A is N20.2°W and the direction of B is N32.5°E. The captain wishes to set a straight course that will result in the ship passing through the midpoint of AB. Calculate:

(a) the distance of M from each of the buoys,

(b) the distance the ship travels from M to the midpoint of AB,

(c) the course the captain must set.

21

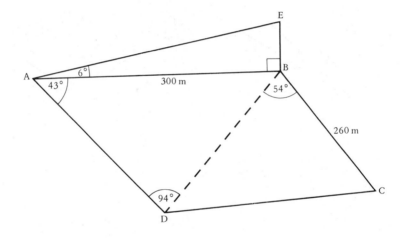

The diagram represents a field ABCD on level ground with a tree EB standing at one corner.

AB = 300 m, BC = 260 m, BÂD = 43°, AD̂B = 94°, and CB̂D = 54°.

The angle of elevation of the top of the tree from A is 6°. Calculate:

(a) the height of the tree,

(b) the lengths of the sides AD, BD and DC,

(c) the area of the field in hectares (1 hectare = 10 000 m²).

Give each answer correct to three significant figures.

22 The diagram represents a building AE at the corner of a horizontal Spanish plaza.

$$AB = 70\,m, \quad AC = 80\,m, \quad A\widehat{B}E = 35°, \quad B\widehat{A}C = 65°,$$
$$C\widehat{A}D = 32° \quad and \quad A\widehat{D}C = 78°.$$

Find, correct to three significant figures:

(a) the height of the building,
(b) the length of BC,
(c) the length of DC,
(d) the area of the plaza, in square metres.

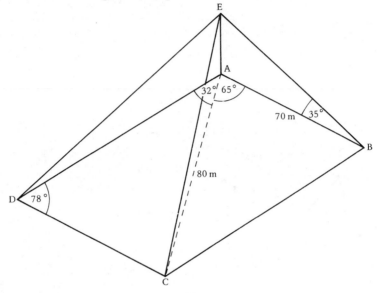

23

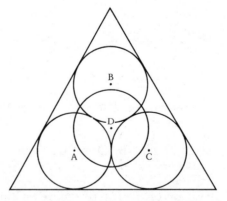

Three similar spheres, each of radius 5 cm, and with centres A, B and C are placed in a box with a triangular base, as shown in the sketch. A fourth identical sphere, centre D, is placed so that it rests in contact with the other three spheres.

(a) Show that ABCD is a regular tetrahedron, and draw a sketch of ABCD with ABC as base.

124

(b) Write down the length of an edge of ABCD.

(c) Find the distance AN, where N is the midpoint of BC.

(d) Find AM, if M is the point on AN such that AM = 2MN.

(e) Given that D is vertically above M, find the height of D above the horizontal base ABC.

(f) Use the result for (e) to find the depth of the box needed to contain the arrangement described above.

Part 2:   Revision Papers 1–24

Revision Paper 1

1   Factorise:
     (a) $6ab + 3bc$ (b) $a(b + c) - d(b + c)$
     (c) $x^2 - x - 6$ (d) $25a^2 - 4b^2$

2   If x is a positive whole number find:
     (a) the values of x that satisfy $5x - 3 < 19$,
     (b) the maximum value of x if $4x + 3 < 24$,
     (c) the minimum value of x if $3x + 2 > 20$.

3   Remove the brackets and simplify:
     (a) $3(a + 2b) + 5(2a + b)$
     (b) $(a + 2b)(2a + b)$
     (c) $3(a + 2b) - 5(a - 2b)$

4   Solve the equations:
     (a) $5x - 3 = 12$ (b) $\dfrac{3x + 1}{2} = 8$ (c) $x^2 = \dfrac{25}{4}$

5

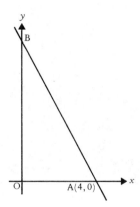

     AB is a straight line with a gradient of -2. If A is the point $(4, 0)$ find:
     (a) the coordinates of B,
     (b) the equation of AB.

6   Three-fifths of John's money is equal to Harry's, and eight-ninths of Harry's is equal to Tom's. If they have a total of £38.40 between them, how much does each have?

7   A polygon with n sides has $\dfrac{n}{2}(n - 3)$ diagonals. Find the number of sides of a polygon which has:
     (a) 35 diagonals,   (b) 77 diagonals.

8   Given that $a = \sqrt{b^2 + c^2}$:

    (a) Estimate, without using a calculator, the value of a when $b = 2.96$ and $c = 4.03$.

    (b) Express c in terms of a and b.

9   (a) The image of the point P under the transformation given by the matrix $\begin{pmatrix} 0 & 1 \\ -1 & 0 \end{pmatrix}$ is the point $(-3, -4)$. Find the coordinates of P.

    (b) Find the image of the point $(4, 7)$ under the transformation given by the matrix $\begin{pmatrix} 2 & 0 \\ 0 & 3 \end{pmatrix}$.

10

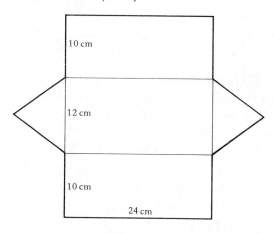

The diagram shows the net for a prism. Calculate:
(a) the area of one of the triangular faces,
(b) the total surface area of the prism,
(c) the volume of the prism.

Revision Paper   2

1   If petrol in France costs $3\frac{1}{2}$ francs per litre, how much per gallon will it cost in England given that 1 litre $= \frac{7}{32}$ gallons and 8 francs $= £1$?

2   A factory employs 70 people, each being paid £110 per week. Management and unions agree to return to work after a strike if there is a 10% increase in the weekly wage but a 10% decrease in the labour force. Find the increase (or decrease) in the total weekly wage bill.

3   The size of each exterior angle of a regular polygon is $x°$ and the size of each interior angle is $8x°$. Find the value of x and the number of sides to the polygon.

4 A car is travelling at x kilometres per hour. How many metres will it travel in m minutes?

5 A metal sphere of radius R cm is melted down and recast, without any change in volume, into spheres of radius $\dfrac{R}{6}$ cm. How many such spheres may be cast?

6 A motorcycle bought for £1260 depreciates in value by 10% each year. What will it be worth when it is three years old? Give your answer correct to the nearest £10.

7 Find the value of k such that:
$$(x - 4)(2x + 3) = 2x^2 + kx - 12$$

8 Find the area on a map of scale $1 : 50\,000$ which represents a farm of area two hundred hectares (1 hectare $= 10\,000$ square metres).

9 In a certain secondary school there are 124 boys in the fourth year. Of these, 64 play soccer, 68 play rugby and 58 take part in athletics; 26 play soccer and rugby, 37 play rugby and take part in athletics; and 30 play soccer and take part in athletics. Six boys participate in none of these activities, whereas x boys take part in all three.

Draw a Venn diagram to illustrate these facts, clearly showing the number in each region in terms of x. Form an equation in x and solve it.

How many boys take part:
(a) in all three activities,
(b) in only one activity,
(c) in exactly two activities?

10 The table gives the speed of a vehicle, v metres per second, at time t seconds after it starts from rest.

t	0	5	10	15	20	25	30	35	40
v	0	9	16	20.2	22	22.8	22.8	22.2	21

Taking 2 cm to represent 5 seconds on the t-axis and 2 metres per second on the v-axis, plot these points on a graph and join them with a smooth curve.

Use your graph to estimate:
(a) the maximum speed of the vehicle and the time at which this occurs,
(b) the acceleration of the vehicle when $t = 15$,
(c) the value of t when the acceleration is zero.

Revision Paper   3

1 If $x = 2 \times 10^5$ and $y = 5 \times 10^4$ find, in the form $a \times 10^n$:

   (a) xy (b) $\dfrac{x}{y}$ (c) $x + y$ (d) $x - y$

2 The size of each exterior angle of a regular polygon is $x°$ and the size of each interior angle is $3x°$. Find the value of x and the number of sides to the polygon.

3 Which two of these have the same value?

$$3^4 \qquad 2^6 \qquad 6^2 \qquad 9^2$$

4 Arrange the numbers $5, -3, -2.95, 2.7$ and $3\frac{1}{2}$ in ascending order.

5 Find the gradient and length of the line segment AB.

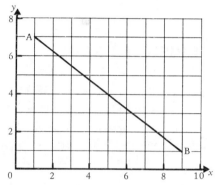

6 A greengrocer buys 6 bags of red potatoes and 5 bags of white potatoes for £25. The following day she buys 4 bags of red together with 8 bags of white for £26. If she pays £x per bag for the reds and £y per bag for the whites on both occasions form two linear equations in x and y and solve them to find the price of each bag.

7 (a) Solve the equation $x^2 - 3x - 10 = 0$.

   (b) Sketch the graph of $y = x^2 - 3x - 10$, showing clearly where it crosses the axes. Draw the axis of symmetry.

8 Amanda bought x first-class stamps at 18p each and y second-class stamps at 13p each. Express each of the following statements as mathematical statements.

   (a) The total number of stamps bought was 40.

   (b) The number of first-class stamps bought was more than twice the number of second-class stamps bought.

   (c) The total cost of the stamps was more than £5.

9 The population of a certain city is known to double every twenty years. In 1900 it was 80 000.

   (a) What was the population in 1960?

   (b) What will it be in the year 2000?

   (c) What was it in 1860?

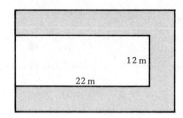

10

A lawn measuring 22 metres by 12 metres is surrounded on three sides by a path of width x metres as shown in the diagram. If the area of the path is 120 m^2 form an equation in x and solve it. What is the total perimeter of the path?

Revision Paper 4

1 (a) The attendance at City's last match was 18 493. Write this attendance correct to 3 significant figures.

(b) The attendance at the last Scotland–England soccer international was 84 000, correct to the nearest 1000. Write down the lowest and highest possible attendances.

2 The takings at a Christmas Fayre amounted to £1470. It was decided to divide the money between the School Minibus Fund and a local charity in the ratio $3:2$. How much did the charity receive?

3 (a) Find the smallest integer which satisfies the inequality $3x - 2 > x + 7$.

(b) Find the largest integer which satisfies the inequality $5x - 13 < x + 4$.

4 One method of solving the equation $x - 20 = \sqrt{x}$, where $\sqrt{x}$ denotes the positive square root of x, is to square both sides and solve the resulting equation.

(a) Use this method to solve the resulting equation.

(b) Do all the answers to (a) satisfy the equation $x - 20 = \sqrt{x}$? Explain what you find.

5 Water increases in volume by 4% when it is frozen. How much water is required to make 1000 cm^3 of ice? Give your answer correct to the nearest whole number.

6 Solve the simultaneous equations:

$$3x + y = 17$$
$$7x - y = 23$$

7

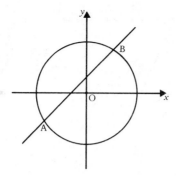

The equations of the circle and straight line shown in the diagram are $x^2 + y^2 = 25$ and $y = x + 1$ respectively. Find:

(a) the coordinates of A and B, the points of intersection of the straight line and the curve,

(b) the coordinates of the points where the circle crosses the axes.

8 A car is sold for £6650 at a loss of 30% of the original purchase price. Calculate the original purchase price of the car.

9

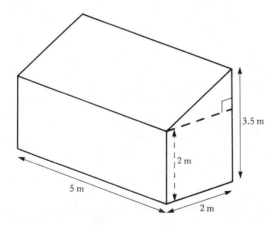

The diagram shows a lean-to shed 5 m long. The near side of the shed is 2 m high and the far side 3.5 m high, its width being 2 m. Calculate:

(a) the ground area on which it stands,

(b) the length of a sloping side of the roof,

(c) the area of cross-section of the shed,

(d) the volume of the shed,

(e) the volume of rain falling on the shed, in m³, during a storm of rainfall 10 cm.

10

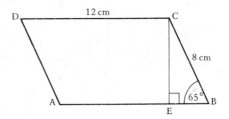

In a parallelogram ABCD, CE is perpendicular to AB, $\widehat{ABC} = 65°$, BC = 8 cm and DC = 12 cm. Calculate, correct to 2 s.f.

(a) the length of BE,   (b) the area of the parallelogram.

Revision Paper   5

1   Seven-twelfths of the pupils in the fourth year at Widdicombe School study geography and ninety-five do not. How many pupils are there in the fourth year?

2   What is the smallest number which, when divided by 8, 12 or 15 leaves a remainder of 11?

3   Solve these equations:

(a) $\dfrac{x-7}{3} = 2$ (b) $\dfrac{x}{3} - 7 = 2$ (c) $\dfrac{3}{x-7} = 2$

4   (a) If: $\mathscr{E}$ = {positive integers less than 15}
                A = {multiples of 3}
                B = {multiples of 4}

list the elements in the following sets:

$$A, \quad B, \quad A \cap B, \quad (A \cup B)'$$

(b) In a group of twenty children, twelve have pens, fourteen have pencils but three have neither. How many children have both a pen and a pencil?

5   The nearest star, Proxima Centauri, is approximately four light years away. If one light year is 9.4×10^{12} km how long would it take to travel to this star in Concorde travelling at 2240 km/h? Give your answer in years in standard form.

6   A two-figure whole number is written down at random. What is the probability that:

(a) the number is greater than 36,

(b) the number is less than 34?

7

The diagrams show a cube in the six different positions so that the numbers 1 to 6 are facing outwards. The cube is now turned to the positions given below. Fill in the missing numbers in the correct relative positions.

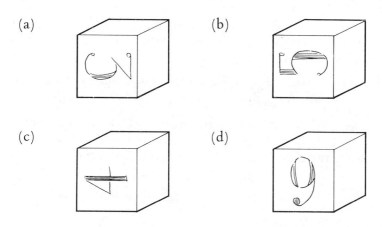

(a)

(b)

(c)

(d)

8   Two cyclists leave Georgetown at noon. One cycles at 10 m.p.h. while the other cycles at $8\frac{1}{2}$ m.p.h. If they follow the same route, how long will it be before they are 3 miles apart?

9   The scale of an Ordnance Survey map is 1:2500. A lake is approximately oval on the map, being 8 cm long and 5 cm wide. Find, correct to three significant figures, the area of the lake in km². (The area of an oval $2a$ long and $2b$ wide is given by the formula $A = \pi ab$. Take $\pi = 3.142$.)

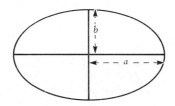

10   A and B are two observation points, 800 m apart, on a straight road that runs in a direction N72°E. From A the bearing of a tower T is N48°E while from B the bearing of the tower is N33°W. Calculate:

(a)   the distance of T from each of the observation points A and B, giving your answers correct to 3 significant figures,

(b)   the shortest distance from the tower to the road,

(c)   the bearing of A from B.

Revision Paper

1 The purchase price of a radio is £27.60. If this includes VAT at 15% find the price of the radio before VAT was added.

2 Given that $E = \frac{1}{2}m(v^2 - u^2)$ find E, correct to three significant figures, when $m = 6.2$, $v = 8.85$ and $u = 5.37$.

3 A wooden table is made from four square legs of side 8 cm and 1 m long, with a rectangular top 220 cm by 90 cm and 3 cm thick. Find the volume of wood used in (a) cm³ (b) m³.

   If 1 cm³ of the wood weighs 0.8 grams, find the weight of wood used in: (c) grams (d) kilograms.

4 A manufacturer sells 16 oz cans of fruit cocktail at 50p and 10 oz cans at 35p. Calculate the price of 1 oz for each can and hence determine which is the better buy: the 16 oz or the 10 oz can.

5 Given $x = \frac{1}{2}\left(t + \dfrac{1}{t}\right)$ and $y = \frac{1}{2}\left(t - \dfrac{1}{t}\right)$ find each of the following in as simple a form as possible:

   (a) $x + y$ (b) $x - y$ (c) $4xy$

6 If $f: x \rightarrow 4x + 3$ and $g: x \rightarrow 2x + k$ find the value of k if fg and gf are the same mappings. Using this value of k find:

   (a) $fg(3)$,   (b) the value of x if $fg(x) = 47$.

7 The diagram shows a square pyramid VABCD. The side of the square base is 5 cm and V is 4 cm above the base.

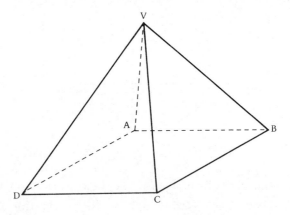

   Draw an accurate net for this solid. From your net find:
   (a) the lengths of the sloping sides VA, VB, VC and VD,
   (b) the distance of V from the side AB.

   What is the volume of this pyramid?

8   When a cold rod is heated, its length increases by 4%. If the length of the rod **after** heating is 44.2 cm, find its length when cold.

9   Draw the unit square OABC, where O, A, B and C are respectively the points $(0,0)$, $(1,0)$, $(1,1)$ and $(0,1)$, together with its image under the transformation T whose matrix is

$$\begin{pmatrix} -1 & -2 \\ -2 & 1 \end{pmatrix}.$$

Describe the effect of the transformation and calculate the scale factor of the enlargement.

10   The skittles for ten-pin bowling are set up in four rows that form an isosceles triangle as shown in the sketch.

How many skittles would be required if there were:

(a)   10 rows   (b)   20 rows?

How many rows would there be if 36 skittles were required?

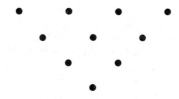

Revision Paper   7

1   The cost of a journey by car varies as the square of the speed of the car. When the speed is 30 m.p.h. the cost is £9. Find the cost of the journey if the speed is increased to:

(a)   40 m.p.h.   (b)   70 m.p.h.

2   If $f = \dfrac{1}{\sqrt{\left(1 - \dfrac{v^2}{c^2}\right)}}$ change the subject to c.

3   A trapezium has a perimeter of 22 cm. The two parallel sides are such that the length of one is three times the length of the other. The non-parallel sides are equal. If the distance between the parallel sides is 4 cm find:

(a)   the lengths of the four sides,

(b)   the area of the trapezium.

4

1	2	3	4	5	6	7	8
9	10	11	12	13	14	15	16
17	18	19	20	21	22	23	24
25	26	27	28	29	30	31	32
33	34	35	36	37	38	39	40
41	42	43	44	45	46	47	48
49	50	51	52	53	54	55	56
57	58	59	60	61	62	63	64

The diagram shows a number square with a rectangle marked on it. This is called the '39 rectangle' since 39 is the number at the base of the rectangle.

(a) Write down the numbers in the '45 rectangle'.

(b) Write down the sum of the numbers in the '59 rectangle'.

(c) Write down, in terms of N, the sum of the numbers in the 'N rectangle'.

(d) Which rectangle has a sum of 135?

(e) Explain why the total of the numbers in a rectangle could not be   (i) 24   (ii) 171.

5   The diagram shows a straight line p which crosses the x-axis at the point $(-2, 0)$ and the y-axis at the point $(0, 2)$. When the line p is reflected in the line whose equation is $x = 2$, its image is the line q.

(a) What is the gradient of the line p?

(b) Copy the diagram and on it draw the line q.

(c) Write down the coordinates of the points where the line q crosses the axes.

(d) Write down the equation of the line q.

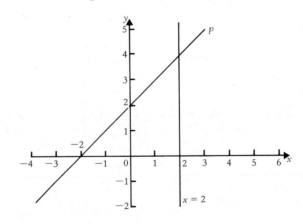

6   Joel is investigating the areas of a set of similar figures. His theory is that the area A (cm^2) of any given figure varies as the square of its base b (cm).

By drawing accurate figures, and counting squares, he finds that $A = 24$ when $b = 4$ and $A = 96$ when $b = 8$.

(a) Do these values confirm his theory?

(b) What is the equation connecting A and b?

(c) What value of A will he expect when $b = 6$?

(d) He wants to draw a figure such that $A = 150$. What length should he use for b?

7   The diagram represents a circular motor-racing track, radius R miles, with A and B the positions of two cars at a particular time on a certain lap. If AB subtends an angle of $\theta°$ at the centre, the arc length AB is given by $\dfrac{\pi R\theta}{180}$.

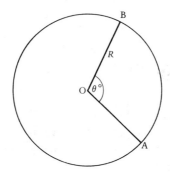

Assuming that the cars are travelling at a constant speed of 176 m.p.h. around a track of radius $\frac{1}{2}$ mile, and that A travels to B in 8 seconds, find the angle subtended by the arc AB at the centre O, giving your answer correct to the nearest tenth of a degree ($\pi = 3.142$).

8   At noon the positions of three aircraft X, Y and Z from an airport control tower, towards which they are flying, are given as 30 miles N67°W, 45 miles N42°E and 60 miles S27°E respectively. If all three aircraft are flying at the same height at a speed of 300 m.p.h. find the position and bearing of Z from Y when X is over the control tower.

9   The points O, A, B and C have coordinates $(0,0)$, $(1,0)$, $(1,1)$ and $(0,1)$ respectively. Draw the image of this square under the transformation T whose matrix is $\begin{pmatrix} 3 & -1 \\ 1 & 3 \end{pmatrix}$.

Describe the effect of this transformation and calculate the factor by which the area of the square has increased.

139

10 The cost, C pounds per square metre, of laying a tarmacadem road is given by $C = x + \dfrac{60}{x}$ where x is the speed, in miles per hour, of the machine.

Corresponding values for x and C are given in the following table.

x	3	4	5	6	7	8	10	12	14	16	18
C	23	19	17	16	15.6	15.5	16	17	18.3	19.8	21.3

Draw a graph to represent this data using 1 cm to represent 1 unit on the x-axis and 1 cm to represent 1 unit on the C-axis.

Use your graph to find the speed at which the machine must travel to keep the cost of laying as small as possible.

Revision Paper   8

1 A shopkeeper buys a light fitting for £54 and adds 35% to make his profit. Value added tax at 15% is then added to this total to give the selling price. Find the selling price giving your answer correct to the nearest 5 p.

2 Given that $b = \sqrt{e^2 - h^2}$, find b, correct to 3 significant figures, when $e = 16.42$ and $h = 12.97$.

3 Shan believes that the relationship between two varying quantities H and V is that V varies as the cube of H. In an experiment she found that $V = 27$ when $H = 6$. What value of V should she expect:
   (a) when $H = 8$ (b) when $H = 4$?

4 Light travels at 3×10^5 kilometres per second. How far will it travel in a year of 365 days?

5 The value of c is given by:
$$c^2 = a^2 + b^2 - 2abx$$

Without using a calculator, and using suitable approximate values for the numbers, find an estimate for the value of c when $a = 8.74$, $b = 3.13$ and $x = 0.5078$.

6   The frequency distribution table given below shows the ages, in complete years, of all the people living in a block of flats.

Age (years)	0–9	10–19	20–29	30–39	40–49	60–99
Frequency	42	28	32	33	40	27

(a) How many people live in the block?

(b) Draw a histogram to illustrate these data.

7   (a) The solutions of the equation $x^2 + bx + c = 0$ are 4 and -5. Find b and c.

(b) If $A = P\left(1 + \dfrac{R}{100}\right)$ change the subject to R and find the value of R when $A = 870$ and $P = 750$.

8   The following examinations have to be time-tabled for the fourth year.

English	$2\frac{1}{2}$ hours
Mathematics	$2\frac{1}{2}$ hours
History	$2\frac{1}{2}$ hours
Geography	3 hours
French	$1\frac{1}{2}$ hours
Chemistry	2 hours
Physics	2 hours
Woodwork	3 hours
Cookery	$1\frac{1}{2}$ hours

There are two sessions each day. The morning session lasts 3 hours while the afternoon session lasts $2\frac{1}{2}$ hours.

No examination is permitted to last longer than the session for which it is time-tabled. English and mathematics are compulsory. No pupil takes both history and geography, and no pupil takes woodwork and cookery.

(a) If the examinations begin on Monday morning when is the earliest that they can end?

(b) Give a possible time-table.

141

9   Two quantities x and y are known to be related by the law $y = a + \dfrac{b}{x^2}$
where a and b are constants. Values obtained in an experiment are given in the following table.

x	3.5	4.2	6	7.3	8.7
y	7.45	6.70	5.83	5.56	5.40

Draw a graph, plotting values of y against those of $\dfrac{1}{x^2}$. Choose scales which maximise the use of your graph paper.

Use your graph to estimate the values of a and b, and hence find the value of y when $x = 5$ and of x when $y = 8$.

10 A transformation P is described by the matrix $\begin{pmatrix} -1 & 0 \\ 0 & -1 \end{pmatrix}$, and a translation Q is described by the vector $\begin{pmatrix} 4 \\ 3 \end{pmatrix}$.

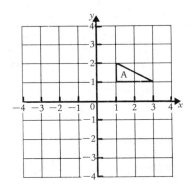

(a) Copy the diagram, and show the image of the triangle A under the transformation P. Mark the image B. Describe this transformation in geometrical terms.

(b) Show the image of B under the translation Q. Mark this image C. Describe in geometrical terms the single transformation equivalent to P followed by Q.

Revision Paper 9

1 Simplify:

   (a) $4^{\frac{3}{2}}$, 4^0, $(\frac{1}{8})^{-\frac{1}{3}}$

   (b) $24a^3b \div 8a^2b^4$

   (c) $\dfrac{1}{2x-1} - \dfrac{6}{2x^2+3x-2} - \dfrac{2}{x+2}$

2 (a) Factorise (i) $2 - \frac{1}{2}a^2$, (ii) $6a^2 + 5a - 6$.

   (b) Evaluate $(5\frac{3}{8})^2 - (2\frac{5}{8})^2$.

   (c) A retailer buys pencils at £x per hundred and sells them at y pence each. Find his profit in pence after selling z pencils.

3 If y varies inversely as the square of x and $y = 3$ when $x = 2$ find:

   (a) y when $x = 3$,   (b) x when $y = \frac{1}{3}$.

4 George Brucker earns £9000 each year. If his allowances which are not taxable amount to £4360, how much tax will he pay when the basic rate is:

   (a) 29%,   (b) 25%,   (c) 33%?

5 (a) Solve the quadratic equation:
$$x^2 - 2x - 15 = 0$$

   (b) Find the value of a such that:
$$x^2 + 10x + 21 = (x+3)(x+a)$$

   (c) Find the value of b such that:
$$x^2 - 36 = (x-b)(x+b)$$

6 When the price of potatoes falls three pence per pound it is possible to buy an extra three pounds for £4.60. Find their original cost per pound, and the number of pounds bought.

7 A lipstick has a mass of 8 grams and costs £1.80. Calculate the cost per kilogram.

8 Draw the graph of $y = \dfrac{12}{x}$ for values of x between -4 and -1 and between 1 and 4. On the same axes draw the graph of $y = 3x + 2$ for values of x between -3 and $+3$. Write down the values of x at the points where the graphs intersect. What equation are these the roots of?

9   Designs in tiles on the floor of an Eastern temple show a cross of red tiles set within a square of white tiles. The extremities of the cross are always at a distance of one tile from the edge of the square. The first two designs are shown in the diagram and the numbers of red and white tiles required for these designs are given in the table.

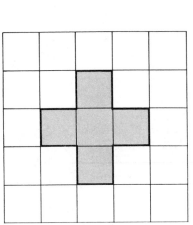
Design number 1

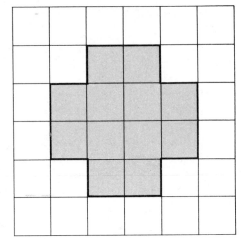
Design number 2

Design number	1	2	3	4	5
Number of tiles used along the side of the square	5	6			
Number of red tiles required	5	12			
Number of white tiles required	20	24			

(a) The pattern is extended for designs 3, 4 and 5. Copy and complete the table.

(b) What entries would be made in this table for design number n?

(c) How many red tiles are required when 52 white tiles are used?

(d) For design number p, twice as many white tiles as red tiles are required. Find the value of p.

10 The table shows the marks of 120 fifth-year pupils in a geography examination. The maximum mark possible is 60.

Mark	1–10	11–20	21–30	31–40	41–50	51–60
Frequency	6	14	22	38	30	10

144

(a) Draw, on the same diagram, a histogram and a frequency polygon, to represent this data.

(b) Complete the following cumulative frequency table.

Mark	$\leqslant 10$	$\leqslant 20$	$\leqslant 30$	$\leqslant 40$	$\leqslant 50$	$\leqslant 60$
Cumulative frequency						

  (i) How many pupils scored 40 or less?
  (ii) How many pupils scored more than 30?
  (iii) What is the probability that a pupil chosen at random scored 30 or less?

(c) Draw a cumulative frequency curve. Use it to find:
  (i) the median mark,
  (ii) the upper and lower quartile marks,
  (iii) the pass mark if 100 pupils passed,
  (iv) the number of distinctions if the mark for a distinction is set at 45.

Revision Paper   10

1 To rent a car for a day in Corfu the rental charges are: a basic charge of 3500 drachmas, plus 500 drachmas for insurance, plus 22 drachmas per kilometre after the first hundred kilometres. When I took delivery in the morning the recorder showed 18 402. After a day touring it read 18 538, and I used it for a 12-kilometre trip in the evening. How much did I have to pay the hire company? If the rate of exchange was 194 drachmas to one pound sterling, how much was this in sterling? Give your answer correct to the nearest penny.

2 A distance recorder gives a correct reading when the tyres have a circumference of 170 cm. If oversize tyres of circumference 175 cm are fitted, what will be the true length of a journey if the recorded distance is 80 km? Give your answer correct to three significant figures.

3 (a) Given $\dfrac{4a - 3b}{2a + 5b} = \dfrac{2}{5}$ find the ratio $a : b$.

  (b) If y varies as $2x^2 - 3$ and $y = 4$ when $x = 2$ find:
    (i) y when $x = -1$,   (ii) x when $y = -\frac{12}{5}$.

4 Simplify:
  (a) (i) $125^{\frac{2}{3}}$ (ii) $(\frac{1}{25})^0$ (iii) $(\frac{1}{25})^{-\frac{3}{2}}$ (iv) $5^{-3} \times 25^{\frac{3}{2}}$
  (b) $24a^5b^2 \div 3a^8b^4$
  (c) $(a^2 + b^2)^2 - (a^2 - b^2)^2$

145

5   The matrix $A = \begin{pmatrix} 5 & 2 \\ -3 & 1 \end{pmatrix}$ represents the transformation T such

that $\begin{pmatrix} x \\ y \end{pmatrix} \to \begin{pmatrix} 5 & 2 \\ -3 & 1 \end{pmatrix}\begin{pmatrix} x \\ y \end{pmatrix}$. Find:

(a) the determinant of A,

(b) the point into which $(5, -7)$ is mapped by the transformation T,

(c) the inverse of A,

(d) the coordinates of the point which is mapped to $(25, -4)$ under the transformation T,

(e) the matrix A^2.

6

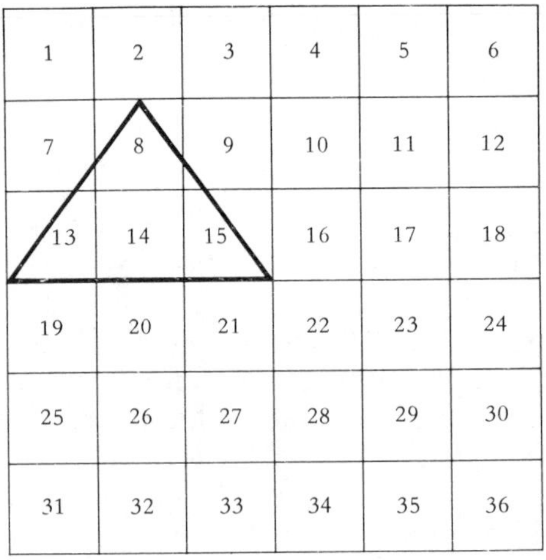

1	2	3	4	5	6
7	8	9	10	11	12
13	14	15	16	17	18
19	20	21	22	23	24
25	26	27	28	29	30
31	32	33	34	35	36

The diagram shows a number square with a triangle marked on it. This is called the '8 triangle' since 8 is the top number in the triangle. The triangle must always remain completely within the number square.

(a) Find the total of the numbers in:
    (i) the 27 triangle,   (ii) the 10 triangle.

(b) Write down, in terms of x, the numbers in the 'x triangle', and find their sum.

(c) Which triangle has a total of 106?

(d) What is:
    (i) the largest value for x,
    (ii) the smallest value for x?

(e) Explain why the total for any triangle could not be
    (i) 43   (ii) 138.

7

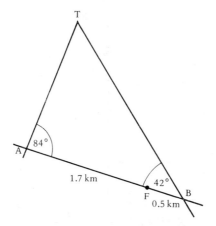

The diagram represents the road layout which enables a farmer to travel from his farm F to the nearest town T via either junction A or junction B. If ∠TAB = 84°, ∠TBA = 42° and the farm is 1.7 km from A and 0.5 km from B, which route is the shorter and by how much?

8

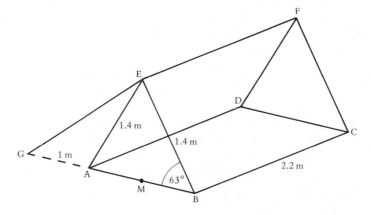

The diagram shows a tent with a rectangular base ABCD of length 2.2 m. The uniform cross-section is in the form of an isosceles triangle with equal sides of lengths 1.4 m, each of which is inclined at 63° to the horizontal. EF represents the ridge of the tent and GE is a guy rope which is attached to the ground at G. G lies on BA produced such that AG is one metre. If M is the midpoint of AB find:

(a) the height of the ridge FE above the ground,
(b) the width, AB, of the rectangular base,
(c) the angle of elevation of F from M,
(d) the angle the guy rope GE makes with the ground,
(e) the volume of rain falling vertically on the tent in a storm of rainfall 8 mm.

   Give your answer in cm³ correct to three significant figures.

9

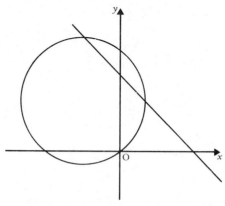

The equations of the straight line and circle shown in the diagram are respectively $x + y = 3$ and $x^2 + y^2 + 7x - 4y = 0$. Find:

(a) the coordinates of the points where the circle crosses the axes,

(b) the coordinates of the points where the straight line and circle intersect.

10 Boxley, Crawton and Danton are three towns on a straight road. A car leaves Boxley at 1 p.m. and travels to Crawton, 80 miles away, at a steady speed of 50 m.p.h. It stops at Crawton for a few minutes before returning to Boxley at a steady speed of $42\frac{1}{2}$ m.p.h. arriving at Boxley at 5 p.m.

A second car leaves Danton, 40 miles further on from Crawton, at 12.30 p.m. and travels without stopping to Boxley at an average speed of 80 m.p.h. It drops its passenger at Boxley and returns to Danton immediately at an average speed of 50 m.p.h. Draw travel graphs for these two journeys and use them to find:

(a) when and where the cars pass each other,

(b) the time the first car leaves Crawton,

(c) the time the second car arrives back at Danton.

Use $2\,\text{cm} \equiv 10$ miles and $4\,\text{cm} \equiv 1$ hour.

Revision Paper 11

1 The five tyres of a car, i.e. the four road tyres plus the spare, were each used equally on a car that travelled 24 000 miles. How many miles were covered by each tyre?

2 The value of a house increases by 10% each year. A house is valued at £50 000 today.

(a) What should it be worth in two years time?

(b) What was it worth two years ago?

Give your answers correct to the nearest thousand pounds.

3 Given that $S = \left(\dfrac{u + v}{2}\right) t$:

(a) Evaluate S when $u = 3.92$, $v = 9.65$ and $t = 6.4$. Give your answer correct to two significant figures.

(b) Express t in terms of S, u and v.

4 ABC is an isosceles triangle in which AC and BC are the equal sides. A is the point $(2, 4)$, B the point $(8, 2)$ and C lies on the straight line with equation $y = 6$. If the x-coordinate of C is a, use Pythagoras' Theorem to find expressions for AC^2 and BC^2 in terms of a. Hence form an equation in a and solve it to find the coordinates of C.

5 Copy and complete the table that follows, so that $C \propto n$.

No. of units of electricity used, n	80	120	188		375	516
Total cost, C (pence)	640			1936	3000	

Can you give a meaning to the constant of proportion?

6 A dictionary with 422 pages is 1.95 cm thick excluding the covers. Calculate the thickness of a single page, giving your answer in mm correct to two significant figures.

7 A car ferry leaves Plymouth at midnight to travel to the Breton port of Roscoff. It sets a course of S20°E from Plymouth and sails at a steady 12 knots for three hours by which time it has reached a point due north of Roscoff. At this point it changes course, sailing due south to Roscoff which it reaches at 9.15 a.m.

Calculate:

(a) the distance sailed before changing course,

(b) the distance travelled by the ferry between the two ports,

(c) the direct distance between the ports.

8 If O is the centre of the circle, $\widehat{ACB} = 51°$ and $\widehat{BEC} = 27°$ find:

(a) $\widehat{BAC}$ (b) $\widehat{ACE}$ (c) $\widehat{CBD}$

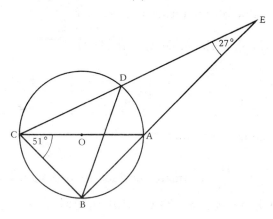

9   A 2×2 transformation matrix M maps the points $(3,1)$ and $(1,3)$ on to $(10,6)$ and $(14,10)$ respectively. Find the matrix.

Use this matrix to find the images of the points $(0,0)$, $(1,0)$, $(1,1)$ and $(0,1)$.

Plot the transformed points on squared paper and determine the area of the resulting figure. Compare this area with that of the given unit square. Compare your answer with the value of the determinant of M.

10

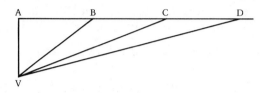

The diagram represents four lamp-posts A, B, C and D which are placed at 50 metre intervals along a straight road which is 15 metres wide. If they are viewed from a point V on the opposite side of the road and immediately opposite A, find $\angle ACV$ and $\angle CVD$.

Revision Paper

12

1   Tickets for seats at a concert are at three prices: £7, £5 and £3. One quarter of the seats are for £7 tickets, one third for £5 tickets and the remaining 845 seats cost £3 each.
(a) How many seats are available?
(b) Find the total amount collected if every ticket is sold.

2   By writing $y = x + 1$ in the equation $ax + by + c = 0$ find the value of x in terms of a, b and c?

What is the value of y in terms of a, b and c?

3   Copy and complete the table so that $A \propto r^2$.

r	0	2		5		10
A		6	24	37.5	96	

What is the equation connecting A and r?

4   Given that $y = \dfrac{10}{\sqrt{x}}$ estimate, correct to one significant figure, the value of y when x is   (a) 24.67   (b) 0.2467.

5   A function f is defined by $f(x) = x^2 - 7x - 18$.

(a) Evaluate: (i) $f(8)$ (ii) $f(0)$.

(b) Find the values of x for which:
   (i) $f(x) = 0$ (ii) $f(x) = -18$ (iii) $f(x) = -30$

6   Draw x and y axes each for values from 0 to 10. Draw the figure ABCD where A is $(1,1)$, B is $(3,1)$, C is $(3,2)$ and D is $(1,2)$.

(a) Find the image of ABCD under the transformation given by the matrix M where $M = \begin{pmatrix} 3 & 0 \\ 0 & 3 \end{pmatrix}$. Mark this image A'B'C'D'.

(b) Find the area of ABCD and the area of the image A'B'C'D'.

(c) Find the value of $\dfrac{\text{area of A'B'C'D'}}{\text{area of ABCD}}$.

(d) Find the determinant of the transformation matrix. What do you notice?

7   Between two elections, the size of the electorate in a constituency increased by 14%. For the second election, 68 001 people were entitled to vote. How many could have voted at the first election?

8

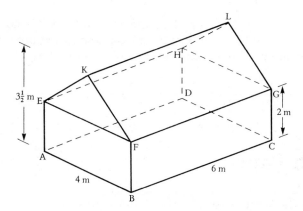

The figure illustrates a shed 4 metres wide and 6 metres long which has a ridged roof $3\frac{1}{2}$ metres above ground level. The shed is 2 metres high at the eaves. Calculate:

(a) the length of KC,

(b) the angle KC makes with the floor ABCD,

(c) the angle between the planes LAB and ABCD.

151

9   Three particles, A, B and C, start simultaneously and move in the plane Oxy as described in the table below.

Particle	Starting point	Direction of movement	Units moved per second
A	$(1,-3)$	Parallel to the positive direction of the y-axis.	2
B	$(2,-6)$	Parallel to the positive direction of the y-axis.	3
C	$(3,c)$	Parallel to the positive direction of the y-axis.	4

At one instant A and B are at points with the same value of y.

(a) How long do the particles take to reach these points?

(b) Find the value of y at each of these points.

(c) At this same instant the particle C has the same value of y as that of the particles A and B. Find c.

10   The value of T is given by the formula:

$$T = 2\pi \sqrt{\frac{a^2 + b^2}{ag}}$$

Without using a calculator, estimate the value of T when $a = 1.97$, $b = 0.98$, $g = 9.81$ and $\pi = 3.14$. Use suitable approximate values for a, b, g and π. Show clearly each stage in your reasoning.

Revision Paper   13

1   Which is the better cash pay rise, and by how much:
    (a) 9% on a weekly wage of £130,

    (b) 7% on a weekly wage of £150?

2   Find the volume of a solid right circular cone of height 9 cm and base radius 4 cm giving your answer in terms of π.

    The cone is now immersed in a cylinder, base radius 16 cm and depth 30 cm, which is half full of water. How much will the surface of the water rise?

3   During the last week of March, 184 cars were tested for defects in brakes, lighting and steering by a garage registered as a Ministry of Transport Vehicle Testing Station. The results are listed as follows: 32 had faulty brakes, 39 had faulty lights and 29 had faulty steering. Eight cars had both brakes and lights faulty, 11 had faulty lights and steering, and 11 had brakes and steering below the required standard. If 109 cars had no faults whatsoever, but x cars had all three defects, form an equation in x and solve it.

How many cars had:

(a) good brakes and lights but poor steering,

(b) exactly one defect,

(c) exactly two defects?

4   The fuel cost per nautical mile ($£C$) for a liner travelling at x knots is given by the expression $C = 0.4x + \dfrac{140}{x}$. Complete the following table which gives values of x and the corresponding values for C.

Speed, x (in knots)	8	10	12	14	16	18	20	22	24
Cost, C (in £s)	20.7		16.5	15.6	15.15	15.0		15.15	15.4

Draw a graph to show how the cost varies for speeds between 8 knots and 24 knots, using 1 cm as 1 unit for x and 4 cm as 1 unit for C. (Use £14 as the lowest value on the C-axis.)

Use your graph to estimate:

(a) the most economical speed and the corresponding cost per nautical mile,

(b) the cost per nautical mile when the speed is 10.3 knots,

(c) the speed when the cost per nautical mile is £16.

5   If 99 is multiplied by multiples of 11 a distinct pattern is evident. Part of this pattern is given below. Study what is given and try to complete the table without using a calculator. Simply look for the pattern.

$$99 \times 11 = 1\ 0\ 8\ 9$$
$$99 \times 22 = 2\ 1\ 7\ 8$$
$$99 \times 33 = 3\ .\ 6\ .$$
$$99 \times 44 = 4\ .\ .\ .$$
$$99 \times 55 = .\ 4\ .\ .$$
$$99 \times 66 = 6\ .\ .\ .$$
$$99 \times 77 = .\ .\ .\ .$$
$$99 \times 88 = 8\ 7\ .\ .$$
$$99 \times 99 = .\ .\ 0\ .$$

153

6

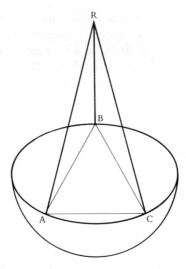

A hemispherical lampshade is suspended from a point in the ceiling by three chains, each of length 35 cm. The chains are attached to three points, A, B and C, on the rim of the lampshade such that ABC is an equilateral triangle. If the angle between each pair of chains is 50° find:

(a) a side of the equilateral triangle ABC,

(b) the diameter of the bowl,

(c) the depth of the bowl.

7 A holiday camp site is in the shape of a quadrilateral ABCD in which AB = 80 m, BC = 100 m, AD = 150 m, ∠BAD = 60° and ∠CBD = 60°. The camp shop (S) is equidistant from AB and AD, and equidistant from CB and CD. Using ruler and compasses only draw a scale diagram taking 1 cm ≡ 10 metres. From your drawing determine:

(a) the length of CD,

(b) the distance of S from B and D,

(c) the distance from S to the furthest point on the camp site.

8

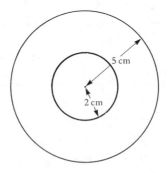

The diagram shows the section through a roll of tissue paper which is 0.1 mm thick. If $\pi = 3.142$ find the length of paper on the roll giving your answer correct to the nearest metre.

9 A rectangle ABCD is inscribed in a circle of diameter 8 cm. If $AB = x$ cm show that $BC^2 = 64 - x^2$. If the area of the rectangle is A cm^2 show that $A = x\sqrt{64 - x^2}$.

Draw the graph of $A = x\sqrt{64 - x^2}$ for values of x from 0 to 8 at unit intervals and at $x = 7.5$. Take 2 cm to represent one unit for x and 4 cm to represent 5 units for A.

Use your graph to find:

(a) the value of A when $x = 4.3$,

(b) the value(s) of x when $A = 24$,

(c) the largest possible value of A and the value of x for which it occurs.

10 Sketch the graphs of the circle and straight line with equations $4x^2 + 4y^2 = 25$ and $2x - 2y - 1 = 0$. Solve the equations to find the coordinates of the points of intersection of the circle and the straight line.

Revision Paper   14

1 A groundsman rolls a cricket ground with a roller 2 metres wide and 90 cm in diameter. If the area of the ground is 1.35 hectares, find:

(a) the number of revolutions made by the roller,

(b) the distance, in metres, travelled by the roller,

(c) the time taken to do the rolling, if the roller travels at 5 km/h. Give your answer in minutes (take $\pi = 3.142$).

2 The value of A is given by the formula $A = 2\pi r(r + h)$.

Without using a calculator, and using suitable approximations for the values of r and h, find, as a multiple of π, an estimate for A when $r = 5.26$ and $h = 14.83$.

3 On a milkman's round 112 customers take milk every day, 43 take at least one product other than milk and 44 customers on some days take nothing at all. What is:

(a) the maximum,

(b) the minimum, number of customers on his round?

4 (a) Find the value of:

(i) $\dfrac{9^{\frac{1}{2}}}{9^{-\frac{1}{2}}}$ (ii) $\left(\dfrac{2}{9}\right)^{0}$ (iii) $\left(\dfrac{1}{27}\right)^{-\frac{2}{3}}$

(b) The curve $y = ax^2 + b$ passes through the points $(2, 3)$ and $(-3, 18)$. Find the values of a and b. Does the curve pass through the points $(4, 5)$ and $(-1, -6)$?

155

5 Find the value of k such that:
$$(x - 5)(3x - 4) = 3x^2 + kx + 20$$

6 Two different numbers are selected at random from the first nine natural numbers. What is the probability that:

(a) the total will be 8,

(b) the total will be either 5 or 7?

7 Peter and June leave Prestley together at 4 p.m. to cycle to Northcott which is 18 miles away. Peter cycles at 15 m.p.h. and June cycles at 12 m.p.h. At 4.10 p.m. Stephen leaves Northcott and cycles along the same route at 14 m.p.h.

Draw an accurate travel graph to show these three journeys. Take 2 cm to represent 10 minutes, and 1 cm to represent 1 mile. Use your graph to find:

(a) the time at which Peter and Stephen pass,

(b) how far both June and Stephen are from Prestley when they meet,

(c) how many minutes elapse between the times that Stephen passes the other two,

(d) the time at which Peter and June are exactly 2 miles apart.

8 Tickets are available at three prices for a series of concerts. On a certain evening n people buy the cheapest tickets at $£x$ each, one third of this number buy the middle-priced tickets which cost three times as much as the cheapest, and for every five sold at this price three of the most expensive tickets are sold, each of which costs half as much again as the middle-priced tickets. In all, 690 people attend the concert paying a total of $£1957.50$. How many people buy the cheapest tickets? What is the cost of the dearest ticket?

9 A scale model of a new car is one-tenth as long as the car. Copy and complete the following table taking care to give your answers in the units asked for.

	Model	Car
Length	47.4 cm	m
Area of windscreen	cm^2	1.155 m^2
Boot capacity	400 cm^3	m^3
Number of wheels		5

10 The eighteenth century mathematician Christian Goldbach stated that every odd number after 7 can be expressed as the sum of three prime numbers. Express (a) 33 (b) 61 (c) 91 as the sum of three primes.

Revision Paper 15

1 A Post Office regulation states that the sum of the length and girth of a parcel to be sent by parcel post must not exceed two metres. I need to send a parcel of maximum size containing thin metal rods each 1.2 metres long. Assuming that there is no wasted space find the width of a side if the parcel has square ends.

If I later decide to use a parcel with circular ends, determine the percentage increase (or decrease) in the number of rods in the parcel (take $\pi = 3.142$).

2 An employee of a large manufacturing company earns £180 per week for a basic 40-hour week. Her union negotiates a 10% rise in her hourly rate, together with a 5% reduction in her basic working week. Find:
(a) her new hourly rate,
(b) the percentage change in her weekly wage,
(c) the payment for 3 hours overtime if the overtime rate is time-and-a-third at the new hourly rate.

3 A greengrocer sells 7 lb bags of mixed vegetables for £1.46. Each bag contains 4 lb of carrots at x pence per lb and 3 lb of parsnips at y pence per lb. When the price of carrots increases by 2 p and parsnips by 6 p he decides to include only 2 lb of parsnips with 5 lb of carrots in each bag. In this way he is able to sell the 7 lb bag at £1.52.

Form two equations in x and y and solve them to find the original price per lb for each vegetable.

4 A particle moves in a straight line in such a way that t seconds after it has left its starting point O, its displacement, d is given by $d = 8t - t^2$. Construct a table to show the values of d for integer values of t from 0 to 9. Plot these points on squared paper, choosing your own scales, and join them with a smooth curve. Use your graph to determine:
(a) when the particle returns to its starting point,
(b) the times at which it is 12 units from O,
(c) the time at which it is momentarily at rest,
(d) its velocity after (i) 2 seconds (ii) 4 seconds.

5 Given that y varies as x^n, write down the value of n in each of the following cases:
(a) y is the area of a rectangle of sides x and $2x$.
(b) y is the surface area of a cube of side x.
(c) y and x are the sides of a rectangle with a constant area.
(d) y is the volume of a rectangular block measuring $3x$ by $2x$ by x.
(e) y is the volume of a cylinder with base radius x and a constant height.

6 The points $O(0,0)$, $A(3,0)$ and $B(3,2)$ are transformed by the matrix M where $M = \begin{pmatrix} 1 & -1 \\ 1 & 1 \end{pmatrix}$, into O, A_1 and B_1 respectively.

(a) Find the coordinates of A_1 and B_1.

(b) Draw, and label on a graph, triangle OAB and its image, triangle OA_1B_1. Take a scale of 2 cm to 1 unit on both axes.

(c) The transformation whose matrix is M can be obtained by combining two separate transformations. By measuring distances and angles on your graph, indicate the nature of these two separate transformations.

7 A sports car is travelling along a straight road and its speed, v metres per second, after time t seconds is given by the following table.

t (in seconds)	0	5	10	15	20	25	30	35
v (in ms^{-1})	0	12.3	23.5	33.7	38	38	34.5	28

Plot these values, taking 4 cm to represent 5 seconds on the time axis and $10\,m\,s^{-1}$ on the speed axis. Draw a smooth curve to pass through these points and estimate from your graph:

(a) the maximum speed of the car and the time after which it is reached,

(b) the times at which the speed of the car is $35\,m\,s^{-1}$,

(c) the acceleration of the car after 10 seconds.

8 In a photograph of the front of St. Paul's Cathedral the building is 10 cm wide, 11.5 cm high and the area of the clock face is $0.567\ cm^2$. If the actual height of the building is 149 metres calculate:

(a) its width, correct to the nearest metre,

(b) the actual area of the clock face.

9 The diagram shows three identical lamp-posts AB, CD and EF equally spaced at 50 metre intervals along a straight road of width 9 metres. A telephone kiosk T is immediately opposite the post AB, and from T the angle of elevation of B is $42°$. Calculate:

(a) the height of a lamp standard,

(b) the angle of elevation of F from T,

(c) the angle CE subtends at the kiosk.

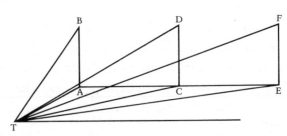

10 The product of three consecutive positive even whole numbers is added to k times the middle number. Find k if the result has the same value as the cube of the middle number.

Revision Paper   16

1 A builder estimates that it will cost him £2400 for labour and £1920 for materials to build a garage. He agrees to build the garage for £5292. His actual costs for labour and materials are 5% higher than he estimated. Find his profit.

2 Show that if the product of three consecutive positive whole numbers is added to the middle number, the result is equal to the cube of the middle number.

3 A shopkeeper adds 20% of the cost of an article to give himself a profit. Value Added Tax at 15% is then added to the total to give the selling price. Find the selling price of an article for which the shop-keeper pays £75.

4 A parallelogram has sides of lengths 5 cm and 9 cm. If the shorter diagonal is 6 cm long calculate:
(a) the angles of the parallelogram,
(b) the length of the longer diagonal,
(c) the area of the parallelogram.

5

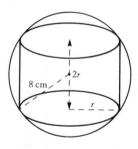

A cylinder whose height is equal to its diameter is cut from a solid sphere of wood of radius 8 cm. Find:
(a) the height of the cylinder,
(b) the volume of wood wasted,
(c) the surface area of the cylinder:
    (i) in cm^2,
    (ii) as a percentage of the surface area of the original sphere
       (take $\pi = 3.142$).

6   A particle is moving with an initial speed of 6 m/s. In the next 3 seconds its speed increases uniformly to 12 m/s and then the speed decreases uniformly until the particle stops moving after a further 5 seconds.

(a) Show this information in a speed–time graph.

(b) Find:
    (i) the acceleration of the particle in the last three seconds of the motion,
    (ii) the total distance travelled by the particle.

7   All the red picture cards are removed from a pack of 52 playing cards. A card is drawn from the remainder. What is the probability that it is:

(a) red,

(b) a black picture card,

(c) an ace,

(d) the Queen of spades,

(e) a red two,

(f) the King of hearts?

8   The spades numbered 1 to 9 are taken from a pack of playing cards and laid face down on a table. First one card, and then a second card are chosen at random from the nine. Draw a probability tree to show the probabilities of drawing odd or even cards. Hence find the probability that:

(a) the first card is odd,

(b) both cards are odd,

(c) both cards are even,

(d) the first card is even and the second is odd,

(e) the first card is odd and the second is even,

(f) one card is odd and one card is even.

9   The function f maps x on to $f(x)$ where $f(x) = x^2 + 2x - 15$ and the function g maps x on to $g(x)$ where $g(x) = 4x - 5$. Find:

(a) $f(-5)$,

(b) $g(3)$,

(c) $f(g(3))$,

(d) $g(f(x))$,

(e) the values of x if f maps x on to 0,

(f) the values of x, correct to two decimal places, if $f(x) = g(x)$.

160

10 The distribution of the ages of the 600 inhabitants of a village is given in the following table.

Age (in years)	Frequency	Age (in years)	Cumulative frequency
0–9	40	<10	
10–19	55	<20	
20–29	70	<30	
30–39	85	<40	
40–49	95	<50	
50–59	95	<60	
60–69	90	<70	
70–79	50	<80	
80–99	20	<100	

Complete the cumulative frequency column and use it to draw a cumulative frequency curve. Use 2 cm to represent 10 years and 2 cm to represent 100 inhabitants.

(a) Use your graph to find:
   (i) the median age for the village,
   (ii) the upper and lower quartiles, and the interquartile range.

(b) If an inhabitant is chosen at random what is the probability that this person:
   (i) is younger than 60,
   (ii) is over 75 years old?

Revision Paper   17

1 Use your calculator to find:
   (a) $\cos 163°$
   (b) x if $\cos x = 0.8247^2$
   (c) x if $\sin^2 x = \dfrac{1}{2.4}$

2 (a) Solve: $\dfrac{x}{12} + \dfrac{2}{5} = \dfrac{x}{3}$
   (b) If $5x = 4y$ find the ratio of x to y.

3 Solve the equation $7x^2 + 2x - 1 = 0$ giving your answers correct to two decimal places.

4 (a) Given that $\dfrac{\sin q}{\sin \phi} = \dfrac{\sin h}{\sin z}$

find q when $h = 40°$, $\phi = 50°$ and $z = 60°$.

(b) Make d the subject of the formula:

$$\dfrac{4\pi^2}{k} = \dfrac{MT^2}{d^3}$$

5 Two similar model railway engines have linear dimensions in the ratio $5:7$. What are the ratios of:

(a) their surface areas,

(b) their volumes?

6 If y varies as the square of x and $y = 4$ when $x = 4$ find:

(a) y when $x = 3$,

(b) x when $y = 6\frac{1}{4}$.

7 (a) Find the smallest integer that satisfies the inequality
$6x - 3 > 2x + 11$.

(b) Find the largest integer that satisfies the inequality
$3x + 11 > 9x - 2$.

8 A function is defined by $f(x) = x^2 + 9x + 14$.

(a) Evaluate:

    (i) $f(1)$ (ii) $f(-3)$

(b) Find the values of x for which:

    (i) $f(x) = 0$ (ii) $f(x) = 14$ (iii) $f(x) = 6$

9 The diagram shows OAB'C', the image of the unit square OABC under a shear. Write down the matrix for this shear. Does this shear preserve area?

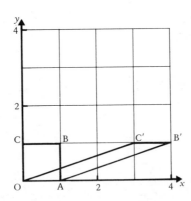

10 Construct a pentagon ABCDE, the vertices of which lie on a circle of radius 6 cm, given that $AB = 8$ cm, $AC = 10$ cm, $BD = 11$ cm and $DE = 9$ cm. Measure and record the lengths of BC and AE.

Revision Paper   18

1 (a) Find the value of k such that $(x + 2)(2x + 1) = 2x^2 + 5x + k$.

   (b) Find the largest integer that satisfies the inequality
       $4x + 3 > 7x - 12$.

   (c) Find the smallest integer that satisfies the inequality
       $10x - 2 > 3x + 48$.

2 (a) If petrol costs 47.3p per litre, how many complete litres can I
       buy for £10?

   (b) Petrol costs 48.9p per litre. What is the smallest number of litres
       I can buy so that I spend an exact number of pence?

3 A triangle ABC is inscribed in a circle such that AB = 7 cm,
   BC = 24 cm and $\widehat{ABC} = 90°$. Find the diameter of the circle.

4 (a) Copy the diagram given below and write down the coordinates
       of the vertices A, B and C.

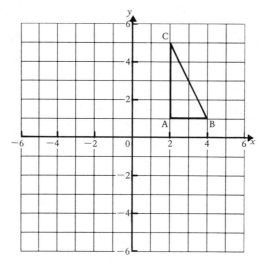

   (b) Write down, as a column vector:
       (i) the translation from A to B, (ii) the translation from B to C.

   (c) Show on your diagram the image of triangle ABC after the
       transformation determined by:
       (i) $S = \begin{pmatrix} 0 & -1 \\ -1 & 0 \end{pmatrix}$ (ii) $T = \begin{pmatrix} -1 & 0 \\ 0 & -1 \end{pmatrix}$

       Label these images $A_1B_1C_1$ and $A_2B_2C_2$ respectively and describe
       each geometrically.

   (d) Describe the single transformation that maps $A_1B_1C_1$ on to
       $A_2B_2C_2$.

5   The value of V is given by the formula $V = \frac{1}{3}\pi r^2 h$. Without using a calculator, estimate the value of V, as a multiple of π, when $r = 9.12$ and $h = 12.8$.

6   Mrs Jones' average weekly grocery bill at present is £44.10 which is 5% more than it was on average each week last year. What was her average weekly grocery bill last year?

7   The first card drawn from a pack of 52 playing cards is the five of spades. What is the probability that the next card drawn is:
    (a) a spade,   (b) a diamond,
    (c) a five,   (d) the five of spades?

8   A motorist buys a car and is told that each tyre should cover 28 000 miles before it is worn out.
    (a) How many miles will she be able to drive before all the tyres, i.e. the four road tyres plus the spare, are worn out?
    (b) At what mileages should she change the tyres around?
    (c) Indicate how the wheels should be changed if it is desirable that each tyre should roll equal distances in opposite directions.
       (Note that if a wheel is removed from one side of a car and placed on the opposite side, its direction of rolling is changed.)

9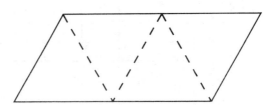

    This net is folded along the dotted lines to form a solid.
    (a) How many edges has the solid?
    (b) How many vertices has the solid?
    (c) What do we call this solid?

10 Part of the graph of the function f which is defined by $f(x) = 6 - \dfrac{12}{x}$

    with domain $\{x \in R,\ x \neq 0\}$ is given opposite.
    (a) From the graph find:
        (i) the value of $f(4.3)$,
        (ii) the value of x for which $f(x) = -5$.
    (b) g is defined by $g(x) = 2x - 7$ with domain the set of real numbers R. Copy the graph for the function f and then draw the graph of the function g for $0 \leqslant x \leqslant 6$.

164

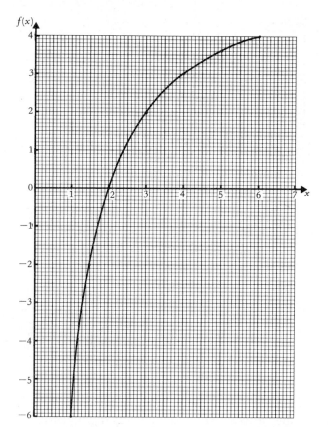

(c) Use your graphs to find the solutions of the equation

$$2x - 7 = 6 - \frac{12}{x}.$$

Give your answers correct to one decimal place.

(d) Show that the equation $2x - 7 = 6 - \dfrac{12}{x}$ can be written in the form:

$$2x^2 - 13x + 12 = 0.$$

Solve this equation without using graphs, giving your answers correct to two decimal places.

Revision Paper   19

1 Find:

   (a) $36^{-\frac{1}{2}}$ (b) 36^0 (c) $9^0 \div 9^{-\frac{1}{2}}$

2 Given that $a + b = 4$ and $ab = 5$, find the value of:

   (a) $a^2 + b^2$ (b) $\dfrac{1}{a} + \dfrac{1}{b}$

3

1	2	3	4	5	6	7	8	9
10	11	12	13	14	15	16	17	18
19	20	21	22	23	24	25	26	27
28	29	30	31	32	33	34	35	36
37	38	39	40	41	42	43	44	45
46	47	48	49	50	51	52	53	54
55	56	57	58	59	60	61	62	63
64	65	66	67	68	69	70	71	72
73	74	75	76	77	78	79	80	81

The diagram shows a number square with an outline ⌐┐ on it.

The number in the lowest square making up this outline is 19 so the outline is 'based on 19'. Using a translation, the outline can be moved so that it is based on a different number, but it must always remain in the same relative position. It cannot be rotated and must always remain completely within the number square.

(a) Find the total of the five numbers in the outline when it is based on (i) 30 (ii) 67.

(b) If the outline is based on x, write down, in terms of x, the other four numbers in the outline and show that the total of the five numbers is $5x - 42$.

(c) Find the five numbers in the outline if their total is 243.

(d) Which numbers in the square cannot be included in any position of the outline?

(e) Explain why the total of the five numbers in the outline could not be (i) 106 (ii) 418.

4 Draw, on the same axes, the graphs of $y = 0.2 + 2\sin x$ and $y = \cos x$ for values of x from $0°$ to $90°$. Take $2\,\text{cm} = 10°$ on the x-axis and 10 cm as one unit on the y-axis.

Use your graphs to estimate the value of x which satisfies the equation $5\cos x - 10\sin x = 1$, giving your answer to the nearest degree.

166

5 (a) Solve the equation $(x-2)^2 = 10$ giving your answers correct to two decimal places.

(b) Solve the equation:

$$\frac{1}{x-1} - \frac{1}{x-2} = \frac{1}{x-3}$$

giving your answers correct to two decimal places.

(c) Two villages A and B are 5 kilometres apart and are linked by a straight road of uniform gradient 1 in x. If their respective heights above sea-level are 100 metres and 260 metres, find x.

6 The total teaching staff (S) in a large school varies as the sum of two parts. The first part varies as the number of pupils (x) in years 1–5, and the second part varies as the number of pupils (y) in the sixth form.

When there are 1100 pupils in years 1–5 and 130 in the sixth form, 60 staff are required, but when there are 792 pupils in years 1–5 and 104 in the sixth form only 44 staff are required. Find the formula connecting S, x and y, and hence find the number of staff required when there are 1342 pupils in years 1–5 and 182 in the sixth form.

7 (a) Exchange rates are such that one pound sterling is equivalent to m deutschmarks and also to f francs. What is the value of x francs in deutschmarks?

(b) Petrol in France costs f francs per litre. Find the equivalent cost per gallon in the United Kingdom if £1 = x francs (1 litre = $1\frac{3}{4}$ pints, 8 pints = 1 gallon).

8 An open rectangular box of volume 32 cm³ has a base in the form of a square of side x cm. Express the height of the box in terms of x and hence show that the total surface area (A) of the outside of the box is given by $A = \left(x^2 + \dfrac{128}{x}\right)$ cm².

Copy and complete the following table which gives values for x and the corresponding values of A.

x	1.5	2	2.5	3	3.5	4	4.5	5
A	87.6		57.5	51.7	48.8		48.7	

Taking 4 cm as 1 unit on the x-axis and as 20 units on the A-axis, draw a graph to show how A changes as x varies from 1 to 5.

Use your graph to estimate:
(a) the minimum value of A,
(b) the side of the largest base giving a total surface area of 50 cm²,
(c) the total surface area when the base has side 1.7 cm.

167

9 Two large trees A and B are 600 metres apart, B being north-east of A. From his farmhouse, F, a farmer observes that the direction of A is N20°W and the direction of B is N32°E. The farmer wishes to build a road which will pass through the midpoint, M, of AB. Calculate:

(a) the distances of F from the trees A and B,

(b) the distance and direction of M from F.

10 The masses, measured to the nearest kg, of 63 boys are listed below.

$$68 \quad 75 \quad 62 \quad 75 \quad 76 \quad 74 \quad 77 \quad 71 \quad 80$$
$$71 \quad 74 \quad 70 \quad 69 \quad 73 \quad 66 \quad 70 \quad 61 \quad 72$$
$$72 \quad 78 \quad 72 \quad 77 \quad 57 \quad 75 \quad 71 \quad 77 \quad 78$$
$$62 \quad 74 \quad 66 \quad 74 \quad 63 \quad 65 \quad 68 \quad 69 \quad 72$$
$$73 \quad 67 \quad 75 \quad 68 \quad 73 \quad 73 \quad 80 \quad 84 \quad 66$$
$$71 \quad 64 \quad 72 \quad 69 \quad 75 \quad 63 \quad 71 \quad 58 \quad 71$$
$$79 \quad 73 \quad 68 \quad 74 \quad 70 \quad 67 \quad 69 \quad 72 \quad 79$$

(a) Use groups 56–60, 61–65, 66–70, 71–75, 76–80, 81–85 to make a frequency table and illustrate the data with a bar chart.

(b) Copy and complete the following cumulative frequency distribution.

Mass (in kg)	< 60.5	< 65.5	< 70.5	< 75.5	< 80.5	< 85.5
Cumulative frequency						

Hence draw the cumulative frequency curve for this data.

(c) Use your curve to find:
  (i) the median,
  (ii) the upper and lower quartiles, and the interquartile range.

(d) What is the probability that a boy chosen at random has a mass in excess of 78 kg?

Revision Paper 20

1 A particle starts from rest. In the next four seconds its speed increases uniformly to 12 m/s and then the speed decreases uniformly until the particle stops after a further eight seconds.

(a) Show this information in a speed–time graph.

(b) Find:
  (i) the acceleration in the last four seconds of the motion,
  (ii) the total distance travelled by the particle.

2 In 1975 it cost £16.32 to produce a food mixer. This cost was made up of materials, labour and administration in the ratio $6:9:2$. By 1988 the cost of materials had increased three times, the cost of labour four times and the administrative costs had doubled. Calculate:

(a) the 1975 cost of labour,

(b) the 1988 cost of materials,

(c) the 1988 cost of the food mixer.

3 Ten judges for an ice-dancing competition award their marks to a competitor as follows.

$$5.7, 5.5, 5.7, 5.8, 5.9, 5.8, 5.4, 5.7, 6.0 \text{ and } 5.5.$$

The competitor's mark is found by neglecting the highest and lowest marks, and finding the average of the remaining marks. What is the competitor's score?

4 A group of young people decide to organise an outing, and agree to share the total cost of £378 equally. Unfortunately two of the boys and a girl are unable to go, so the remainder agree to pay an extra 60p each to make up the lost income. How many young people actually made the trip?

5 Two brothers, David and Jonathan stand at A and B, two points 220 metres apart on a straight path which runs in a direction N63°E. David sights a folly (C) in a direction N32°E which proves to be due north of M, the midpoint of AB. Calculate:

(a) David's distance from the folly,

(b) the distance of the nearest point (N) of the path from the folly,

(c) the distance Jonathan must walk to arrive at N.

6 The points $O(0,0)$, $A(3,0)$ and $B(3,2)$ are transformed by the matrix M, where $M = \begin{pmatrix} 2 & 0 \\ 0 & 2 \end{pmatrix}$, into O, A_1 and B_1.

The points O, A_1 and B_1 are now transformed using the matrix M', where $M' = \begin{pmatrix} 0 & -1 \\ 1 & 0 \end{pmatrix}$, into O, A_2 and B_2.

(a) Find the coordinates of (i) A_1 and B_1, (ii) A_2 and B_2.

(b) Draw axes for x and y such that $-8 \leqslant x \leqslant 8$ and $-8 \leqslant y \leqslant 8$. Use 1 cm as 1 unit on both axes. On your graph, draw and label triangles OAB, OA_1B_1 and OA_2B_2.

(c) Evaluate the matrix M_1 where $M_1 = M'M$.

(d) The original points O, A and B are transformed by the matrix M_1, into the points O, A_3 and B_3. How does triangle OA_3B_3 compare with triangle OA_2B_2?

(e) Draw on your graph the reflection of triangle OA_2B_2 in the x-axis. Label it OA_4B_4. Find the matrix of the transformation under which OA_2B_2 is mapped to OA_4B_4.

7 The equations of the curve and straight line given in the diagram are respectively $2x^2 + y^2 + y - 6 = 0$ and $y = x + 2$.

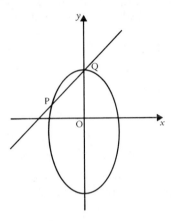

Find the coordinates of:

(a) the points at which the curve crosses the axes,

(b) the points of intersection of the curve and the straight line.

8 Derek Connah wishes to build a rectangular workshop using the party wall with the adjacent property as one side. He decides that he has sufficient bricks – each brick is $\frac{1}{4}$ m long and $\frac{1}{8}$ m wide – to use 61 in each course, the first course of bricks to be laid at the corners as shown in the diagram.

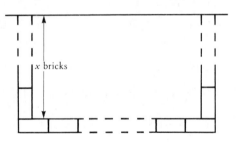

If the interior of the workshop is x bricks wide, how many bricks long will it be? Show that the internal area of the floor of the workshop, A m², is given by $A = \frac{1}{8}x(30 - x)$.

Complete the following table to find the values for A corresponding to the given values for x.

x	0	4	8	12	14	16	18	20	24	28	30
$A = \frac{1}{8}x(30 - x)$	0	13	22	27		28		25	18	7	

Draw the graph of $A = \frac{1}{8}x(30 - x)$ for values of x from 0 to 30. Take 1 cm to represent 2 units for x and for y.

Use your graph to find:

(a) the area of the workshop if it is 11 bricks wide,

(b) the maximum area of the workshop and the corresponding value of x.

Draw the line of symmetry on your graph. What is the equation of this line?

Without making any calculations write down the value of A when x is:

(i) 6   (ii) 26

9   An express train from Cardiff to London is time-tabled to travel the 147 miles at an average speed of 70 m.p.h. If it is six minutes late leaving Cardiff by how much must it increase its average speed if it is to arrive on time?

10

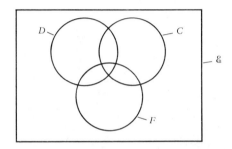

Twenty-one pupils were asked if they had attended a disco (D), a cinema (C) or a football match (F) during the previous week. Every-one had attended at least one, but no one all three. Copy the Venn diagram and shade the areas which represent the *two* empty sets.

It was also recorded that: 5 had been to a cinema, 15 had been to a disco, 9 had attended a football match, 1 had been to both a cinema and a football match, and 3 had been to see a football match but had not gone to either of the others. How many pupils attended a cinema and went to a disco?

Revision Paper   **21**

1   In a cricket match between England and Australia, Australia led on the first innings by 103 runs. In the second innings Australia scored twice as many as England scored in the first, and England scored three times as many as they did in their first innings, thereby winning the match by 53 runs. Find the number of runs scored by each side in each innings.

2   Two cars move around a Scalextric track in concentric circles. The inner car moves in a circle of radius 60 cm and travels at 1 metre per second, while the outer car moves in a circle of radius 70 cm. Find the speed of the outer car if they start and finish a complete circuit of the track together.

If the cars exchange tracks and their speed remain unchanged, find how many laps the leading car is ahead after it has completed 10 laps of the track ($\pi = 3.142$).

3

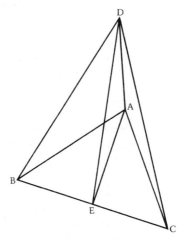

ABC is a horizontal triangle with AB = AC = 5 cm and $\angle$BAC = 80°. D is a point 8 cm vertically above A, and E is the midpoint of BC. Calculate:

(a) the length of BC,   (b) the length of DE,   (c) the angle DEA.

4   Three particles P, Q and R start simultaneously and move as described in the table.

Particle	Starting point	Direction of movement	Units moved per second
P	$(-7, -1)$	Parallel to the positive direction of the x-axis	2
Q	$(17, 1)$	Parallel to the negative direction of the x-axis	4
R	$(r, 2)$	Parallel to the positive direction of the x-axis	3

At one instant P and Q are at points with the same values of x.

(a) How long will the particles take to reach these points?

(b) Find the value of x at each of these points.

(c) At this same instant the particle R is at a point with the same value of x as that of the other two particles. Find the value of r.

5   A car travels 12 kilometres per litre of petrol. The petrol tank holds 42 litres. A driver sets out on a journey of 600 kilometres with a full tank.
    (a) How far can he travel before he requires petrol?
    (b) If he plans to stop just once for petrol, between what distances from the start must he stop?

6   The integers 2 to 9 can be written as fractions in which every digit, except 0, appears once and only once. For example,

$$3 = \frac{17496}{5832}$$

    Form similar fractions for 2 and 5.

7

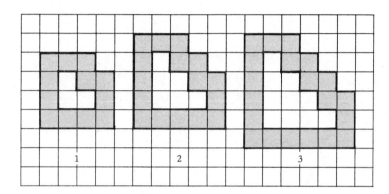

Diagram 1 shows three white tiles in the form of an L, surrounded by red tiles. Diagrams 2 and 3 show how the pattern develops.
    (a) Copy the diagrams and add the next two in the pattern.
    (b) Find a rule which gives the number w, of white tiles, and the number r, of red tiles, for the nth diagram in the pattern.
    (c) Use your rule to find:
        (i)   the number of white tiles when there are 40 red tiles,
        (ii) the number of red tiles when there are 91 white tiles.
    (d) Is there any value of n for which the number of red tiles is equal to the number of white tiles?

8   A rectangular concrete block is x cm wide, $\frac{3x}{2}$ cm high and y cm long, *all dimensions being whole numbers*. The total length of all the edges of the block is 180 cm, and the total surface area of the block is 1192 cm². Form two equations in x and y and hence show that x satisfies the equation:

$$19x^2 - 450x + 2384 = 0$$

    Factorise this equation and hence find:
    (a) the dimensions of the block,   (b) the volume of the block.

9   The diagram shows a number rectangle with a triangle marked on it. This is called the '40 triangle' since the bottom right-hand number in it is 40.

(a) Find the total of the numbers in the '23 triangle'.

(b) Write down, in terms of n, the three numbers in the 'n triangle'. Show that the total of these numbers is $3n - 7$.

(c) Which triangle has a total of 152?

(d) Explain why the total of the three numbers in any triangle could not be (i) 138 (ii) 158.

1	2	3	4	5	6
7	8	9	10	11	12
13	14	15	16	17	18
19	20	21	22	23	24
25	26	27	28	29	30
31	32	33	34	35	36
37	38	39	40	41	42
43	44	45	46	47	48
49	50	51	52	53	54

10   ABCD is a square with E, F, G and H points on AB, BC, CD and DA respectively such that:

$$\frac{AE}{EB} = \frac{AH}{HD} = \frac{CF}{FB} = \frac{CG}{GD} = \frac{1}{2}$$

Prove that EFGH is a rectangle and find:

(a) $\dfrac{\triangle AEH}{\triangle ABD}$

(b) $\dfrac{\text{Area of rectangle EFGH}}{\text{Area of square ABCD}}$

Revision Paper   22

1   A retailer buys a articles at a total cost of £x. He finds that b of the articles are faulty and throws them away but sells the remainder at y pence each thereby making a profit of $p\%$ on the whole transaction. Express y in terms of the other quantities.

2   The scale of a map is $1:50\,000$. Find:
   (a) the distance, in kilometres, between two places which are 15 cm apart on the map,
   (b) the actual area of a farm which covers an area of $4.84\,cm^2$ on the map. Give your answer in (i) km^2 (ii) hectares.

3   Carpets bought by a retailer at £18 per square yard are marked up by 40% before being offered for sale. If 1 yard = 0.91 metres, calculate the selling price per square metre, giving your answer correct to the nearest 10 p.

4   The cost of hiring a concrete mixer is a fixed charge of £N with an additional charge of £M for each day of the hire period.
   (a) Write down an expression for hiring the machine for 4 days.
   (b) When the number of days is x, the total cost is £C. Write down a formula for C in terms of N, M and x.
   (c) When the hire period is exactly seven days there is a reduction in the hire charge of 20%. Find the hire charge for one week.

5   Draw the graph of $y = 2x^2 - 5x + 1$ for values of x from -2 to 4 taking 2 cm as 1 unit for x and 1 cm as 1 unit for y.

   Using the same scales and axes draw the graph of $y = 8 - 2x$. Use your graph to solve:
   (a) $2x^2 - 5x + 1 = 0$ (b) $2x^2 - 3x - 7 = 0$

6   VABCD is a pyramid with vertex V and a square base ABCD of side 10 cm. If $VA = VB = VC = VD = 8\,cm$ calculate:
   (a) the angle VAB,
   (b) the angle BVD,
   (c) the angle VME, if M is the midpoint of AB and E is the point of intersection of the diagonals AC and BD.

7   (a) If y varies as the square of x and $y = 16$ when $x = 2$ find:
       (i) y when $x = 3$,   (ii) x when $y = 1$.
   (b) Given that $a + b = 2$ and that $a^2 + b^2 = 10$ show, without finding the values of a and b, that $ab = -3$. Hence find $(a - b)^2$.

175

8   Thirty-two children in a class were asked which of the subjects geography, cookery and woodwork they were studying. Their replies gave the following information.

17 studied geography

13 studied woodwork

5 studied cookery only

4 studied geography and cookery

3 studied woodwork and cookery

2 studied all three

Two pupils did not study any one of these subjects.

Assuming that x pupils studied geography and woodwork but not cookery, draw a Venn diagram to show these data. Form an equation in x and solve it. Use this value of x to determine:

(a) the number of pupils studying woodwork only,

(b) the number of pupils studying exactly two of these subjects.

9   If the average speed of a car is increased by 8 m.p.h. the time taken for a 240-mile journey is reduced by one hour. Find the original average speed of the car.

10 A train leaves station A for station B and for the first four minutes accelerates such that its speed at various times is as given in the table.

Time, t, after leaving A (in seconds)	0	30	90	150	240
Speed, s (in m s^{-1})	0	$4\frac{1}{2}$	$12\frac{3}{4}$	$17\frac{1}{2}$	20

For the next five minutes it travels at a constant speed of $20\,\mathrm{m\,s^{-1}}$ then retards uniformly over a period of three minutes to stop at station B.

Draw a speed–time graph for the journey, taking 2 cm as one minute on the t-axis and 4 cm as 5 m s^{-1} on the s-axis.

Use your graph to estimate:

(a) the acceleration of the train when $t = 2\frac{1}{2}$ min,

(b) the constant retardation,

(c) the distance between the stations in kilometres, correct to one decimal place.

1 (a) Factorise:
     (i) $3x^2 - x - 2$ (ii) $9x^2 - 3x$
  (b) If $(3x - 5)(x + 4) = 3x^2 + kx - 20$ find the value of k.
  (c) Solve the equation $(x - 2)^2 = 10$ giving your answers correct to two decimal places.

2 (a) A 3-kilowatt electric kettle takes $2\frac{1}{2}$ minutes to boil 3 pints of water. If a unit of electricity (i.e. 1 kilowatt hour) costs 5 p, find the cost of boiling the water.
  (b) A cylindrical candle of diameter 8 cm and height 10.5 cm burns at the rate of 20 cm³ per hour. How long will it burn? (Take $\pi = \frac{22}{7}$ and give your answer correct to the nearest hour.)

3 (a)

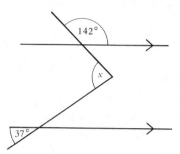

    Find the angle marked x.

  (b)

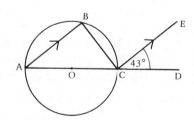

    Find the angles of the triangle ABC.

4 Of the 122 members of a youth club, 54 like table tennis (T), 61 like snooker (S) and 62 like darts (D). 23 like table tennis and snooker, 22 like table tennis and darts, and four times as many like snooker and darts as like all three. If x members like all three and 8 do not like any of the three, draw a Venn diagram to illustrate this information.

  (a) Hence form an equation in x and solve it to find the number of members who like all three activities.
  (b) How many members
     (i) like snooker but neither table tennis nor darts,
    (ii) like just one of these activities?

5   A store sells both metric and imperial sets of drills. The imperial sizes go from $\frac{1}{8}$ inch to 1 inch in steps of $\frac{1}{16}$ inch. The metric sizes go from 3 mm to 25 mm in steps of 1 mm. (Assume 1 inch = 25.4 mm.)

(a) What is the next size up after (i) $\frac{1}{2}"$ (ii) $\frac{5}{8}"$?

(b) What is the next size down from (i) $\frac{1}{4}"$ (ii) $\frac{3}{4}"$?

(c) How many drills are there in an imperial set?

(d) What is the size next but one up from $\frac{3}{8}"$?

(e) What is the size next but two down from $\frac{7}{8}"$?

(f) Which imperial drill is in the middle of the range?

(g) How many drills are there in a metric set?

(h) Which is the nearest metric drill below $\frac{5}{8}"$?

(i) Which is the nearest metric drill above $\frac{3}{4}"$?

(j) Which is the nearest metric drill to $\frac{3}{8}"$? Is this drill larger or smaller than $\frac{3}{8}"$?

6

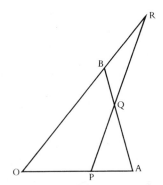

In triangle OAB, $\overrightarrow{OA} = a$ and $\overrightarrow{OB} = b$. P is the point on OA such that $OP = \frac{2}{3}OA$, and Q is the point on AB such that $AQ = \frac{2}{3}AB$. When the lines PQ and OB are produced they meet at R.

(a) Express, in terms of a and b, the vectors:

   (i) $\overrightarrow{OP}$ (ii) $\overrightarrow{PA}$ (iii) $\overrightarrow{AB}$ (iv) $\overrightarrow{AQ}$ (v) $\overrightarrow{PQ}$

(b) By considering triangle OPR and assuming that $\overrightarrow{PR} = m\overrightarrow{PQ}$ show that Q is the midpoint of PR and that $OR = \frac{4}{3}OB$.

A function $f(x)$ is defined as: $f(x) = x^2 + 6x + 27$

(a) Evaluate:
    (i) $f(2)$ (ii) $f(-3)$

(b) Find the values of x for which:
    (i) $f(x) = 27$ (ii) $f(x) = 19$

8   A washing machine may be bought for £246 cash or by paying a deposit of £66 followed by 24 monthly payments of £9.60. Find the total hire-purchase price. How much is saved by paying cash?

178

9   A cyclist leaves a town A at noon to cycle to a town B 50 miles away. He cycles at 15 m.p.h. for $1\frac{1}{2}$ hours, then rests for 15 minutes before proceeding to B at the same speed. A second cyclist leaves A at 12.30 p.m. and cycles to B, without stopping, at a steady speed of 14 m.p.h. At 1.45 p.m. a motorcyclist leaves A and travels directly to B at a steady 60 m.p.h. Taking 4 cm $\equiv$ 10 miles and 4 cm $\equiv$ 1 hour draw the travel graphs for the three journeys. Use your graphs to find when and where the motorcyclist passes the cyclists.

10 The table shows the interest received on £100 invested at 11% compound interest for different periods of time.

No. of years	0	2	4	6	8
Interest (to the nearest £)	0	23	52	87	130

(a) Using 2 cm to represent 1 year on the horizontal x-axis and £10 on the vertical y-axis draw an interest–time graph to represent the compound interest obtained over the 8-year period.

(b) On the same sheet, using the same scales and axes, draw the interest–time graph to represent the interest obtained on £100 invested at 11% simple interest over the same period.

(c) Use your graphs to find:
   (i) the compound interest on £100 invested at 11% for $6\frac{1}{4}$ years,
   (ii) the gain in investing £100 for 7 years at 11% compound interest rather than 11% simple interest.

Revision Paper   24

1   A couple pay £40 000 for their house and £20 000 for their car. The house increases in value by 15% each year whereas the car depreciates each year by the same percentage. How much will each be worth after two years?

2   The exterior angle of a regular polygon is $2x°$ and the interior angle is $7x°$. Find the value of x and the number of sides in the polygon.

3   A particle starts from rest and its speed increases uniformly to 12 m/s in 8 seconds. It travels at this constant speed for a further 10 seconds before the speed decreases uniformly until the particle comes to rest after a further 5 seconds.

Illustrate this information on a speed–time graph. Use your graph to find:

(a) the deceleration in the last 5 seconds,

(b) the total distance travelled by the particle.

4 The scale of an Ordnance Survey map is 1 : 50 000. A farm is represented on the map as a shape whose perimeter is 10 cm and whose area is 6 cm².

(a) Find the perimeter of the farm in kilometres.

(b) Find the area of the farm in (i) square metres, (ii) hectares.

5

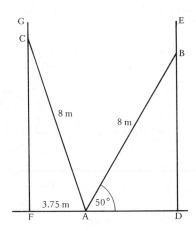

The diagram shows two positions, AB and AC, for a ladder which is 8 m long and rests on level ground between two vertical walls DE and FG. When resting against DE the ladder makes an angle of 50° with the horizontal, and when resting against FG the foot of the ladder is 3.75 m from the base of the wall. Calculate:

(a) the distance of B and C above the ground,

(b) the angle BAC,

(c) the horizontal distance between the walls.

6 A machine produces two types of screws. Long screws are produced at the rate of x per minute whereas the machine will produce 20 more short screws than long screws each minute.

(a) Write expressions for the number of seconds taken to produce each type of screw.

(b) If it takes $\frac{1}{10}$ second longer to produce a long screw than a short screw, write down an equation in x and solve it. How long does it take to produce a short screw?

7 Joan and Jane each roll an ordinary die. The number on each top face is then noted. What is the probability that:

(a) they each roll a six,

(b) Jane scores exactly three more than Joan,

(c) neither of them rolls an odd number,

(d) the sum of their scores is 4,

(e) Joan scores twice as many as Jane?

8   Draw triangle ABC on graph paper where A, B and C are respectively the points $(3, 1)$, $(4, 3)$ and $(7, -1)$. Use a scale of 1 cm to represent 1 unit on each axis.

(a) Find and draw the image of triangle ABC under a transformation represented by the matrix S where $S = \begin{pmatrix} -1 & 0 \\ 0 & 1 \end{pmatrix}$. Describe this transformation.

(b) Find and draw the image of triangle ABC under a transformation represented by the matrix T where $T = \begin{pmatrix} -0.6 & 0.8 \\ 0.8 & 0.6 \end{pmatrix}$.

(c) Show that the points $(1, 2)$, $(2, 4)$ and $(-1, -2)$ are unchanged under the transformation T. Plot these points on your diagram. What is the equation of the straight line on which these points lie?

(d) Describe the transformation T.

9   (a) Copy and complete the table which gives values of $\dfrac{x^2}{2} + \dfrac{2}{x}$ for values of x from 0.5 to 4.

x	0.5	1	1.5	2	2.5	3	3.5	4
$\dfrac{x^2}{2}$	0.13		1.13		3.13		6.13	8
$\dfrac{2}{x}$	4		1.33		0.8		0.57	0.5
$\dfrac{x^2}{2} + \dfrac{2}{x}$	4.13		2.46		3.93		6.70	8.5

(b) Hence draw the graph of $y = \dfrac{x^2}{2} + \dfrac{2}{x}$ for values of x from 0.5 to 4. Use a scale of 4 cm to represent 1 unit on the x-axis and 2 cm to represent 1 unit on the y-axis.

(c) Using the same axes and scales draw the graph of $y = \tfrac{3}{4}x + 2$.

(d) Write down the values of x at the two points where the graphs intersect.

(e) Show that these graphs enable you to find two approximate solutions to the equation $2x^3 - 3x^2 - 8x + 8 = 0$, and write down these solutions.

Would you expect this equation to have any other solutions? Give a reason for your answer.

181

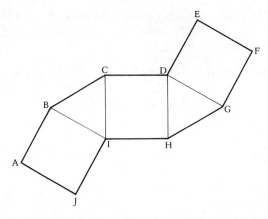

This net can be folded to make a triangular prism. All edges are the same length. When the net has been folded to make the solid, which point coincides with E?

Calculate:

(a) the angle between ABIJ and the base CDHI,

(b) the angle between BJ and HM, where M is the midpoint of CI.

Part 3: Aural Tests 1–10

The following ten tests are aural tests. You should not attempt to do them as you read this book. Your teacher may read them for you to write down your answers, or you could ask another student or adult to read them to you. The intention is that you should spend about twenty seconds on each question. These tests are fairly straightforward. They are intended to introduce you to aural work.

Aural Test

1 Write eighteen thousand and twenty-seven as a number.

2 Fifty marbles are shared equally amongst eight children. How many marbles does each get and how many are left over?

3 How many faces has a cube?

4 My season ticket costs twenty-four pounds each month. If its price increases by ten per cent how much more must I pay?

5 The four angles of a quadrilateral are equal. What kind of quadrilateral is it?

6 What is seventy per cent of one hundred and fifty?

7 The bases of two similar triangles are in the ratio one to three. What is the ratio of their areas?

8 Two cubes have edges in the ratio two to three. What is the ratio of their volumes?

9 Write down the three other angles of a parallelogram given that one angle is one hundred and eight degrees.

10 What is seven to the power zero?

11 What is the cost of a four pound piece of meat if the price is seventy five pence per pound?

12 Write down two thousand four hundred centimetres in metres.

13 Two angles of a triangle are $45°$ and $95°$. Write down the size of the third angle.

14 Write down the positive square root of two and a quarter.

15 Find the hypotenuse of a right-angled triangle whose other sides are six centimetres and eight centimetres long.

16 Write down, as a single number, five squared plus six squared.

17 Write down the number that is exactly halfway between one and a quarter and three and three-quarters.

18 A fish weighs a pound plus half its weight. What is the weight of the fish?

19 A typist charges eighteen pounds for four hours work. What would be the charge for seven hours work?

20 What time is one thirty-five p.m. on the twenty-four hour clock?

Aural Test

1 Reduce eighty by forty per cent.

2 How many edges are there to a cube?

3 What is ten minus seven point four nine?

4 What is the square root of one point four four?

5 The length of a table is two thousand and sixty-five millimetres. Give this length in metres.

6 Write down the cube root of sixty-four.

7 How many axes of symmetry does an equilateral triangle have?

8 Arrange the digits 5, 3, 7, 1, 4 to make the largest possible odd number.

9 I travel for forty minutes at an average speed of sixty miles per hour. How far do I travel?

10 Estimate, in metres, the height of the door through which you came into the room.

11 New York time is five hours behind London time. When it is twelve noon in New York what time is it in London?

12 Correct to the nearest hundred, five thousand, four hundred spectators attended a hockey match. What is the largest number that could have been present?

13 A rectangle is one metre longer than it is wide and has an area of twenty square metres. How wide is it?

14 Divide thirty pupils into two groups so that one group contains twice as many as the other.

15 Write down the number that is exactly halfway between minus two and plus six.

16 With three darts I scored: treble nineteen, ten and thirteen. What was the total score?

17 In a sale a coat priced at eighty pounds is marked twenty per cent off. How much must I pay for it?

18 The ratio of the area of two similar triangles is nine to four. What is the ratio of the lengths of corresponding sides?

19 Is five centimetres more than two inches?

20 How many days are there after the twentieth of September but before the twelfth of October?

Aural Test

1 What is seventy-eight plus fifty-four?

2 What is the value of four to the power minus one half?

3 A pyramid has a square base. How many edges does it have?

4 Express fifty-four square centimetres in square millimetres.

5 A piece of wood forty-nine centimetres long is divided into two pieces whose lengths are in the ratio four to three. How long is the shorter piece?

6 Is five litres more than one gallon?

7 One angle of a parallelogram is seventy-five degrees. Write down the values of the other three angles.

8 The opposite angles of a trapezium measure one hundred and fifteen degrees, and sixty-two degrees. What values do the other two angles have?

9 What is one point two divided by nought point nought four?

10 Which is further: three kilometres or two miles?

11 How many axes of symmetry does an isosceles triangle have?

12 Express sixty pence as a percentage of two pounds.

13 Eighty-four per cent of the five hundred seats on a train are taken. How many seats are vacant?

14 What is the average of forty-two, sixty and seventy-eight?

15 Reduce twenty pounds by thirty per cent.

16 Write nought point nought one four in standard form.

17 A cylinder, a cone and a hemisphere have equal radii and heights. Which solid has the smallest volume?

18 Twenty books were bought for ten pounds sixty and sold for twelve pounds forty. What was the profit on one book?

19 Find the average of eight years six months, ten years four months and nine years two months.

20 The cooking time for a chicken is twenty minutes per pound plus twenty minutes. How long does a ten pound chicken require?

Aural Test

1 A town has a population of three thousand and seventy-eight. Write down this number in figures.

2 Write down the square of nought point six.

3 How many edges are there to a tetrahedron?

4 A wine bottle contains seventy centilitres. How many glasses containing eight centilitres may be filled from this bottle? How much is left over?

5 The price of a dress marked forty-four pounds is reduced by twenty-five per cent in a sale. How much must I pay for it?

6 Write in algebraic form three times x subtracted from four times y.

7 A train travels thirty-six miles in thirty minutes. Express its speed in miles per hour.

8 Sketch the graph whose equation is $y = x + 2$.

9 Two cubes have edges in the ratio two to three. What is the ratio of their surface areas?

10 What is the commission on five thousand pounds at five per cent?

11 Michelle works thirty-seven and a half hours in a five day week. She works the same number of hours each day. How long is her normal working day?

12 The Brickbuilt Building Society pays nine and a half per cent interest per annum. I invest four thousand pounds with them for three months. How much interest will I receive?

13 Express two centimetres as a percentage of five centimetres.

14 The time in Los Angeles is eight hours behind the time in London. What time is it in London when it is 8 a.m. in Los Angeles?

15 Sue Andrews was born in July 1920 and died in November 1985. How old was she when she died?

16 The area of a rectangle is one square metre. If one side is fifty centimetres long what is the length of the other side?

17 The tank of a diesel engine contains ninety litres of fuel. If it uses twelve litres each hour for how long will it run?

18 How long is it from seven thirty a.m. to ten fifty p.m.?

19 Which three consecutive whole numbers add together to give thirty-six?

20 Fencing posts are erected at three-metre intervals. How many posts are required for sixty-three metres of fencing?

Aural Test 5

1 How many seconds are there in half an hour?

2 Express sixty per cent as a decimal fraction.

3 If eight kilometres is equivalent to five miles how far is sixty-four kilometres in miles?

4 Is two pints more than a litre?

5 Express two hundred and seventy square millimetres in square centimetres.

6 Write five hundred and sixty-seven millimetres correct to the nearest centimetre.

7 Share forty sweets between two people in the ratio three to two.

8 A car travels one hundred miles in two and a half hours. Express its average speed in miles per hour.

9 How many minutes are there from eleven thirty-six to two twenty-one?

10 What time is two thirty a.m. on the twenty-four hour clock?

11 Write down an approximate value for thirty-nine multiplied by forty-one.

12 The area of a trapezium is twenty square centimetres. The sum of the parallel sides is ten centimetres. What is the distance between the parallel sides?

13 How many axes of symmetry does a square have?

14 Give twenty-four centimetres as a percentage of sixty centimetres.

15 If one adult and three half-price fares cost ten pounds, what is the cost of one adult fare?

16 How many times is four greater than nought point five?

17 Arrange the digits 2, 0, 9, 5, 3 to make the largest possible number.

18 Sketch the graph whose equation is $y = x^2$.

19 An aircraft travels eighteen hundred kilometres in one hour. How far will it travel in one minute?

20 Which three consecutive even numbers add together to give forty-eight?

Aural Test

1 Tickets for an international match cost £5 each. What is the cost of nine tickets?

2 Thirty thousand eight hundred people attended a rock concert. Write this in numbers.

3 How many corners are there to a rectangular block?

4 Peter bought two records. One cost three pounds forty and the other five pounds seventy. How much did Peter spend altogether?

5 Sixty-two per cent of the pupils in a school are boys. What percentage are girls?

6 What is nought point seven multiplied by nought point six?

7 A milkman started out with four hundred and fifty-six pints and returned with eighty-seven. How many pints had he delivered?

8 Write down the cube of three.

9 Express nought point six seven as a percentage.

10 Five miles is equivalent to eight kilometres. How far, in miles, is forty-eight kilometres?

11 I hired a television set for six months at eleven pounds forty per month. What was the total rental charge?

12 One pupil is to be chosen at random from two boys and four girls. What is the probability that the chosen pupil is a girl?

13 Is one kilogram more than two pounds?

14 I complete a journey of thirty-six kilometres in three hours. What is my average speed?

15 How many axes of symmetry does a rectangle have?

16 Three-quarters of a sum of money is ninety pence. Find the whole amount.

17 Which three consecutive odd numbers add together to give fifty-one?

18 Increase one pound seventy-six by one hundred per cent.

19 Write down the numbers between one and thirty that have both three and four as factors.

20 Write down the first six prime numbers.

1 What is the area of a picture frame measuring twelve centimetres by eight centimetres?

2 Write down the number that is exactly halfway between three eighths and a half.

3 How many eighteen-pence stamps can be bought for three pounds?

4 The area of a rectangle is seventy-two square centimetres. If one side is nine centimetres how long is the other?

5 How many minutes are there in three-quarters of one hour forty minutes?

6 Write down the cube root of twenty-seven.

7 The circumference of a wheel is nine centimetres. Estimate, to the nearest whole number, the diameter of the wheel.

8 How many corners has a cube?

9 Write twenty-four centimetres in metres.

10 In a game of darts I score sixty-three with my first three darts. If I am playing three hundred and one up, how many remain to be scored when the sixty-three has been subtracted?

11 I arrive at the bus-stop at three thirty for a bus due at a quarter to four. If the bus arrives three minutes early how long do I have to wait?

12 Simplify two x minus three x plus five x.

13 A factory with one hundred and twenty employees is to increase the workforce by twenty per cent. How many new employees will they take on?

14 How many edges does a triangular pyramid have?

15 Taking eight kilometres to be equivalent to five miles, estimate forty-two kilometres in miles.

16 One pupil is chosen at random from a group of four boys and three girls. What is the probability that the pupil is a girl?

17 What is nine squared minus four cubed?

18 The first day of April is a Saturday. How many Mondays are there in this particular month?

19 An aircraft flying due east turns clockwise through two hundred and seventy degrees. In what direction is it now flying?

20 Which is the better buy for potatoes: five kilograms for forty-two pence or three pounds thirty for a fifty kilogram bag?

Aural Test

1 How many faces has a triangular prism?

2 The angles of a triangle are $x°$, $2x°$ and $3x°$. What is the size of the smallest angle in degrees?

3 The diameter of a wheel is three centimetres. Estimate, in centimetres to the nearest whole number, the circumference of the wheel.

4 What is the square of nought point five?

5 How many twenty-five pound units of National Savings Certificates could I buy for four hundred and fifty pounds?

6 Tom gets paid 'time and a half' for overtime. How much will he get paid for three hours overtime if his basic rate of pay is four pounds fifty per hour?

7 Express forty per cent as a fraction.

8 What is the sum of the exterior angles of any polygon?

9 In school the morning session finishes at eleven forty-five and the afternoon session starts at ten past one. How long is the lunch break?

10 I live one point six eight kilometres from school. Write down this distance correct to one decimal place.

11 What is the cost of four loaves of bread at fifty-five pence per loaf?

12 Write down, as a single number, seven squared minus five squared.

13 Betty bought a one kilogram bag of sugar and used eight hundred and fifty grams. How many grams remained?

14 Amer can get an eighty per cent mortgage to buy a house costing twenty thousand pounds. How much must he find himself?

15 Ten lamp-posts in a straight line are equally spaced, thirty metres apart. How far is it from the first post to the last?

16 How many thirteen-penny stamps may be bought for two pounds?

17 Write down an approximate value for fifty-eight point seven multiplied by nineteen point three.

18 The dimensions of a rectangle are each a whole number of centimetres. If the perimeter is twenty-four centimetres what is the largest possible area of the rectangle?

19 Train fares increased by ten per cent. If the new fare is one pound thirty-two pence what was the old far?

20 Two representatives are to be chosen at random from eight girls and three boys. If the first chosen is a boy what is the probability that the second will be a girl?

1   If five meals cost sixty pounds, how much will three cost at the same rate?

2   How many grams are there in fifty-six per cent of two kilograms?

3   A square has an area of sixty-four square centimetres. Find the perimeter in centimetres.

4   What is five fifties plus three thirties?

5   What is the next number in the sequence: 2, 4, 7, 11, 16, ...?

6   How many days are there from the twenty-fifth of May to the fifth of June inclusive?

7   John scores thirteen out of twenty in a test. What percentage is this?

8   The height of a triangle is eight centimetres and its area is seventy-two square centimetres. Find the length of its base.

9   Multiply fifty by one and four-fifths.

10 Eight per cent of a sum of money is sixteen pence. Find the whole amount.

11 Two angles of a triangle are sixty-seven degrees and fifty-eight degrees. What is the third angle?

12 The circumference of a wheel is thirty-three centimetres. Give an approximate value for its radius.

13 Bob Johnson was born in November 1902 and died in January 1986. How old was he when he died?

14 The first day of March is a Wednesday. How many Saturdays are there in this particular month?

15 Mostyn saves forty pence each week. How long will it take him to save five pounds?

16 By how many seconds is fifty-six seconds more than three-quarters of a minute?

17 Which three consecutive whole numbers have a product of five hundred and four?

18 Of the twelve girls in a class eight take physics and seven take chemistry. What is the largest possible number of girls taking neither subject?

19 How many axes of symmetry does a sphere have?

20 A part for a car costs twenty pounds plus value added tax at fifteen per cent. How much must I pay for it?

1   Write three thousand, eight hundred and seventy-six correct to the nearest hundred.

2   A record bought for five pounds is sold for six pounds. What is the percentage profit?

3   The exterior angle of a regular polygon is thirty degrees. How many sides does the polygon have?

4   A piece of timber sixty-three centimetres long is divided into two parts in the ratio 5 : 2. How much longer is the one part than the other?

5   What is five and one-eighth minus three and a quarter?

6   A card is drawn at random from a pack of fifty-two playing cards. What is the probability that it is a picture card?

7   The time in Perth (Australia) is eight hours ahead of the time in London. A Test Match starts at eleven a.m. in Perth. What time is this in London?

8   What is the average of thirty-seven, nineteen and forty-six?

9   Today is Tuesday the fourth of February. What date will it be a week next Friday?

10 Imran must pay tax at twenty-nine pence in the pound on sixty pounds of his income. How much tax must he pay?

11 A retailer buys a pair of trousers for sixteen pounds and sells them at a loss of thirty per cent. Find the selling price.

12 A rectangular block measures four centimetres by three centimetres by two centimetres. Find its total surface area.

13 What is the cube of four minus the cube of two?

14 If I drive my car at a steady forty-five miles per hour how long should it take to cover two hundred and twenty-five miles?

15 The hire charge for a roof rack for a car is a basic two pounds fifty plus fifty pence a day. How much will it cost to hire for a week?

16 The bottom of a rectangular tank measures twenty centimetres by ten centimetres. If one litre of water is poured into the empty tank how deep is the water?

17 What is the square root of nought point one six?

18 Find the reflex angle to an angle of thirty-eight degrees.

19 A piece of card measures forty centimetres by thirty centimetres. What is the greatest number of circles with diameters of ten centimetres that can be cut out of this piece of card?

20 How many axes of symmetry does a rhombus have?

Answers

Basic Number Work   1

1 (a) 60, 75   (b) 36, 49
   (c) −19, −25   (d) 125, 216
   (e) $\frac{6}{7}, -\frac{7}{8}$ (f) 0.01, 0.001
   (g) 15a, 18a (h) $5a^4, 6a^5$

2 (a) 3   (b) $\frac{7}{4}$
   (c) $-\frac{13}{12}$ (d) $\frac{5}{7}$

3 (a) 8.07, 8.1, 8.107, 8.70
   (b) $\frac{2}{3}, \frac{3}{4}, \frac{19}{24}, \frac{5}{6}$
   (c) $\frac{1}{3}, \frac{2}{5}, 0.46, \frac{7}{15}$
   (d) $1\frac{1}{4}$, 1.26, $1\frac{2}{5}$, 1.45

4 (a) $\frac{3}{5}$, 0.58, $\frac{4}{7}$, 0.5
   (b) $\frac{8}{3}$, 2.64, $2\frac{5}{8}$, $2\frac{1}{2}$
   (c) 2.5, $\sqrt{6}$, 2.1, $\sqrt[3]{8}$
   (d) $\frac{5}{16}$, 0.28, $\frac{1}{4}$, $\frac{7}{32}$

5 (a) 16   (b) $\frac{1}{9}$ (c) 1
   (d) 4   (e) $\frac{3}{2}$ (f) $\frac{1}{25}$
   (g) 4   (h) $\frac{1}{27}$

6 (a) $4\frac{2}{15}$ (b) $2\frac{3}{4}$ (c) $\frac{3}{4}$
   (d) $5\frac{11}{14}$ (e) $2\frac{13}{20}$ (f) 4
   (g) $\frac{10}{39}$ (h) $1\frac{1}{2}$

7 (a) 2.69   (b) 0.132   (c) 5.3
   (d) 0.04   (e) 0.32   (f) 0.47
   (g) 0.01   (h) 0.5   (i) 93.6
   (j) 0.73

8 (i) 2940, 2937.47, 2940
   (ii) 100, 98.40, 98.4
   (iii) 10, 5.09, 5.09
   (iv) 600, 600.84, 601

9 (a) 3   (b) 4   (c) 400
   (d) 0.04

10 (a) 11   (b) 6   (c) −10
   (d) −25   (e) 10   (f) 3
   (g) −5   (h) 15

11 (a) $3 \times 3 \times 5 \times 5$
   (b) $2 \times 2 \times 3 \times 5 \times 7$
   (c) $2 \times 3 \times 7 \times 13$
   (d) $2 \times 2 \times 2 \times 3 \times 3 \times 19$

12 $2^2 \times 3^2 \times 7^2$, 42

13 (a) 15 : 20   (b) 56 : 16
   (c) 57p : 95p
   (d) 186 cm^3 : 465 cm^3

14 (a) 4×10^3 (b) 8×10^6
   (c) 7.3×10^{-2} (d) 3.5×10^4
   (e) 8.6×10^4 (f) 5×10^5
   (g) 6.8×10^{-7} (h) 5.297×10^2

15 (a) 4.6×10^7 (b) 9.6×10^7
   (c) 6×10^3 (d) 4.83×10^1
   (e) 2×10^6 (f) 3.01×10^2

Problems Involving Number Work   2

1 9.3×10^7 miles
2 1.5×10^8 km
3 5.9×10^{12} miles
4 5.83×10^{12} miles, 4.17×10^9 hours
5 (a) 4×10^5 (b) 2020
   (c) 1915   (d) 2.83×10^5
6 $84.5 \leqslant$ length < 85.5
7 (a) 87 000   (b) 87 500
   (c) 87 500
8 (a) 54 500   (b) 55 499
9 549
10 (a) 11, 60, 61   (b) 13, 84, 85
   (c) 17   (d) 144
   (e) 19, 181
11 (a) 11 + 13   (b) 17 + 17
   (c) 19 + 23   (d) 19 + 31
   (e) 29 + 41
12   1 7 21 35 35 21 7 1
     1 8 28 56 70 56 28 8 1
     1 9 36 84 126 126 84 36 9 1
13 36, 45, 55

14 51, 70
15 (a) (i) 12   (ii) 14   (iii) 26
   (b) $2n + 6$
   (c) (i) 126   (ii) 242
16 (a) (i) Yes
       (ii) Completes on her fifth lap
       (iii) 8, 7
   (b) She only lands on 3, 6, 9
       and 12
   (c) 1, 5, 7 and 11
17 (a) (i) 58   (ii) 103
   (b) $x - 6, x - 12, x - 13, x - 11$
   (c) 19, 20, 21, 26, 32
   (d) (i) No; It would be outside
          the number square
       (ii) Yes
       (iii) Yes
       (iv) No; There is no whole
            number value of x that
            gives $5x - 42 = 85$

18 (a) (i) 180 (ii) 128
    (b) $x + 1, x + 5, x + 6$
    (c) (i) 19 (ii) 39
    (d) 188, 44
    (e) 16, 1
    (f) (i) Does not give a whole
            number value for x
        (ii) Value of x would be
             outside the number
             rectangle

19 (a) 13, 19, 20, 21, 27 (b) 85
    (c) (i) 2, 8, 9, 10, 16
        (ii) 34, 40, 41, 42, 48
    (d) $5n$
    (e) the '40' rhombus
    (f) (i) Yes
        (ii) No (107 not divisible
             exactly by 5)
        (iii) No — goes out of number
              square
20 (a) 8   (b) 4   (c) 156

Parallel Lines, Angles and Triangles 3

1 $a = 63°, b = 63°, c = 73°$
2 $d = 89°$
3 $e = 173°$
4 $f = 66°$
5 $g = 32°, h = 58°$
6 $i = 37°, j = 74°, k = 32°$
7 $l = 101°$
8 $m = 23°, n = 23°, p = 47°$

9 $q = 102°, r = 45°, s = 12°$
10 $t = 43°, u = 81°$
11 $v = 26°, w = 116°$
12 $x = 54°, y = 27°$
13 $a = 72°, b = 72°$
14 $c = 46°, d = 62°$
15 $e = 70°, f = 42°$
16 $g = 63°, h = 57°, i = 60°$

Polygons 4

1 (i) 72°, 108°   (ii) 60°, 120°
   (iii) 45°, 135° (iv) 40°, 140°
   (v) 36°, 144°   (vi) 30°, 150°
   (vii) 15°, 165°

2

No. sides	Exterior angle	Interior angle
8	45°	135°
12	30°	150°
18	20°	160°
20	18°	162°
24	15°	165°
15	24°	156°

3 (a) Yes   (b) Yes   (c) Yes
   (d) No
4 93
5 88°, 113°, 113°, 113°, 113°
6 90°, 60°, 30°
7 Two at 74°, four at 143°
8 111°
9 81°
11 120°
12 132°, 30°, 18°
13 (a) 100° (b) 170°
14 (a) 108°, 120°, 135° (b) B
15 30, 12

Scale Drawings 5

1 901 m, N23.3°W
2 65.70 m
3 (a) 169 m   (b) S74°E (106°)
4 (a) 81 m and 50 m   (b) 31 m
5 74 cm, 115 cm
6 (a) 124 m, 110 m   (b) 74°

7 N50°W (310°), 22 minutes
8 9.3 km in a direction S10°E (170°)
9 (a) 25 m, 27.8 m
   (b) 13 m
10 (a) 25 m
    (b) 32 m (to nearest metre)

Percentages

6

1 £468	2 £51	3 £300
4 1440	5 2.3 kg	6 £2.24
7 (a) £818		(b) £204.50
(c) £122.70		
8 $66\frac{2}{3}\%$		9 144
10 £16 380, £2		
11 (a) £7200		(b) £5832
12 £73 000		13 £28
14 £960		15 £171.39
16 £32		17 £173.60

18 4 yrs	19 7%
20 £59.90	21 £187.19
22 £120	23 £184
24 £37.66	25 £39.20, 28%
26 (a) £21 760	(b) £55 053
27 £1584	28 £176
29 Yes	30 £480
31 £48.60	32 £86.08
33 £22.37, 11%	34 £570.20
35 £9.72, £11.66	36 £26.35

Indices

7

1 (a) 3   (b) $\frac{1}{3}$ (c) $\frac{1}{9}$
   (d) $\frac{1}{9}$

2 (a) 2   (b) $\frac{1}{4}$ (c) 1
   (d) $\frac{1}{16}$

3 (a) 2   (b) 4   (c) 8
   (d) 2

4 (a) 2   (b) 16   (c) $\frac{1}{16}$
   (d) $\frac{1}{8}$

5 (a) 5   (b) 25   (c) 1
   (d) $\frac{1}{125}$

6 (a) $\frac{1}{4}$ (b) 1   (c) 16
   (d) 4

7 (a) 343   (b) $\frac{1}{7}$ (c) 7
   (d) $\frac{1}{49}$

8 (a) 27   (b) 3   (c) 729
   (d) $\frac{1}{27}$

9 (a) $\frac{1}{8}$ (b) $\frac{1}{16}$ (c) 2
   (d) $\frac{1}{2}$

10 (a) $\frac{1}{100}$ (b) $\frac{1}{10}$ (c) 1
   (d) 10

11 (a) $\frac{1}{8}$ (b) 1   (c) $\frac{1}{4}$
   (d) 16

12 (a) 3   (b) 27   (c) 6
13 (a) $\frac{1}{2}$ (b) $\frac{1}{2}$
14 (a) 6   (b) 8
15 (a) a^5 (b) a^8 (c) a^3
   (d) a^4
16 (a) x^7 (b) x (c) x^3
   (d) x^{12}
17 (a) x^4 (b) x^6 (c) x^3
   (d) x^6
18 (a) $\dfrac{1}{x^6}$ (b) 1   (c) $9x^2$
   (d) $x^{7/2}$
19 (a) $x^{5/2}$ (b) x^2 (c) x^{10}
   (d) $\dfrac{1}{16x^2}$
20 (a) 1   (b) a^4 (c) $3a^2b$
21 2^6 and 4^3
22 $4^{1/2}$ and $16^{1/4}$

The Straight Line

8

1 (a) $y = -x$ (b) $y = \frac{1}{2}x + 1$
   (c) $y = 2$ (d) $y = x - 1$
   (e) $x = -2$ (f) $y = 3x - 2$

2 (a) 4, 3   (b) $-3, 5$
   (c) $\frac{1}{3}, \frac{2}{3}$ (d) $\frac{3}{5}, -1$
   (e) $-\frac{3}{2}, 2$ (f) $\frac{5}{3}, -\frac{7}{3}$

3 (a) $y = 2x + 5$ (b) $y = -x + 4$
   (c) $2y = x - 6$ (d) $2y = x + 6$
   (e) $y = 4x + 14$ (f) $3y = -4x + 12$
   (g) $y = 2x$ (h) $7y = -2x + 17$
4 (a) $(0, -2)$ (b) $m = \frac{4}{3}, c = -2$
   (c) 10 units
5 (a) $(8, 0)$ (b) $(0, 10)$
   (c) $m = -\frac{5}{4}, c = 10$

6 E(6, 0), F(1, 0), 42.5 square units

7 (a) 4   (c) −4
   (d) $y = -4x - 4$

8 (a) A(−3, 3), B(−3, −3), C(5, −3)
   (b) 6, 8 and 10 units
   (c) AC = 10 units (Pythagoras)
   (d) $-\frac{3}{4}$

9 (a) A(−2, 1), B(1, 4), C(5, 0)
   (b) 1, (0, 3), $y = x + 3$
   (c) −1   (d) −1
   (e) Since $AC^2 = AB^2 + BC^2$,
      $A\widehat{B}C = 90°$
   (f) 90°
   (g) 12 square units

10 $m = -2, c = 8.$ Lines intersect
   at (2, 4)

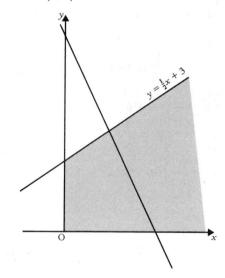

11 (a) A(0, 5), B(15, 5), C(5, 0)
   (b) $-1\frac{1}{2}$
   (c)

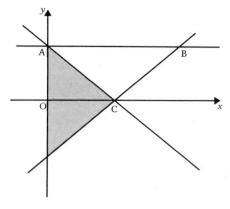

12 (a) I: $x + y = 2$, II: $x = 2$,
       III: $y = 4$, IV: $y = 2x$
   (b)

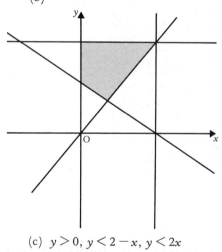

   (c) $y > 0, y < 2 - x, y < 2x$

Simultaneous Linear Equations   9

1 $x = 5, y = 3$	**2** $x = 3, y = -1$	**21**	15p, 20p
3 $x = 2, y = -2$	**4** $x = 4, y = -1$	**22**	Pen 30p, Pencil 12p
5 $x = 1, y = 4$	**6** $x = 4, y = -1$	**23**	Small 32p, Large 56p
7 $x = 2, y = 3$	**8** $x = 3, y = -2$	**24**	Soft £1.75, Hard £3.10
9 $x = -1, y = 3$	**10** $x = -2, y = 2$	**25**	24, 37
11 $x = 3, y = 2$	**12** $x = 2, y = -4$	**26**	Petrol £2.10, Oil 60p
13 $x = 3, y = -3$	**14** $x = 4, y = 3$	**27**	Lime 60p, Orange 50p
15 $x = 1, y = 2$	**16** $x = 6, y = 2$	**28**	Coffee £1.75, Tea 80p, £2.55
17 $x = 5, y = -3$	**18** $x = 6, y = -3$	**29**	£8 (£5 + £3)
19 10 yrs	**20** 11 yrs	**30**	£6.10, £2.85, £47.60

Algebraic Fractions

1 $x(x + 4)$
2 $x(x - 8)$
3 $2a(4a - 1)$
4 $9b(b + 3)$
5 $(x + 3)(x + 4)$
6 $(x + 1)(x + 5)$
7 $(x + 2)(x + 7)$
8 $(x + 2)(x + 5)$
9 $(a + 4)(a + 7)$
10 $(b + 2)(b + 3)$
11 $(m + 6)(m + 7)$
12 $(n + 3)(n + 9)$
13 $(x + 4)(x - 3)$
14 $(x + 5)(x - 3)$
15 $(x + 7)(x - 2)$
16 $(4 - a)(5 + a)$
17 $(b - 7)(b + 4)$
18 $(6 - m)(2 + m)$
19 $(t - 9)(t + 2)$
20 $(x - 3)(x - 5)$
21 $(x - 7)(x - 2)$
22 $(6 - x)(5 - x)$
23 $(a - 5)(a - 4)$
24 $(b - 2)(b - 1)$
25 $(c - 7)(c - 8)$
26 $(y - 4)(y - 7)$
27 $(2x + 1)(x + 2)$
28 $(3x + 1)(x + 3)$
29 $(5x + 2)(x + 5)$
30 $(3b + 7)(b + 2)$

31 $(4a + 3)(a + 5)$
32 $(5a + 1)(a + 4)$
33 $(2x + 1)(x - 2)$
34 $(3x + 2)(x - 5)$
35 $(5x + 1)(x - 3)$
36 $(5a + 4)(a - 2)$
37 $(3 - a)(2 + 7a)$
38 $(3x + 4)(2x + 1)$
39 $(5x + 2)(2x + 3)$
40 $(4x + 1)(7x + 2)$
41 $(3a + 2)(5a + 4)$
42 $(2b + 1)(7b + 6)$
43 $(2x + 1)(3x - 4)$
44 $(5x + 2)(2x - 3)$
45 $(x + 3)(x - 3)$
46 $(x + 5)(x - 5)$
47 $(2x + 5)(2x - 5)$
48 $(3x + 4)(3x - 4)$
49 $(a + 1)(b + 1)$
50 $(2m + 3)(n + 2)$
51 $2(d + 1)(c - 1)$
52 $(2n - 1)(m + 2)$
53 $(5 - 2y)(4 + y)$
54 $2(4 - 3x)(1 + 2x)$
55 $(x + y)(a - b)$
56 $(a - b)(x - 2y)$
57 $(y + 3)(3x - 2)$
58 $(a + b)(c + 2)$
59 $(n - 1)(m + 2)$
60 $(a - 2)(b + 3)$

Quadratic Equations 1

1 3, 5
2 4, 7
3 $-4, 2$
4 $-2, 5$
5 $-3, -4$
6 $-5, -8$
7 $\frac{1}{2}, 3$
8 $\frac{2}{3}, 7$
9 $\frac{2}{3}, 2\frac{1}{2}$
10 $1\frac{3}{4}, \frac{2}{3}$
11 $-\frac{1}{4}, 3$
12 $-\frac{2}{3}, 5$
13 $-\frac{3}{7}, -\frac{2}{5}$
14 $-1\frac{1}{4}, -3\frac{1}{3}$
15 $0, -5$
16 $0, 7$
17 $-2, 2$
18 $-5, 5$
19 $0, 7$
20 $0, -9$
21 $-5, 5$
22 $-4, 4$
23 $1, 13$
24 $1, 12$
25 $-2, -4$
26 $-4, -3$
27 $0, 1\frac{1}{3}$
28 $0, -1\frac{1}{5}$

29 -5 (twice)
30 9 (twice)
31 $\frac{1}{3}, 4$
32 $-2, \frac{1}{7}$
33 $-1\frac{1}{2}, \frac{1}{4}$
34 $-\frac{1}{5}, 4$
35 $-3, \frac{1}{2}$
36 4, 5
37 $-1, 3$
38 3 (twice)
39 2, 4
40 2, 6
41 5, 12
42 8 m
43 9 cm, 12 cm, 15 cm
44 193 cm^2
45 1 m
46 46 years
47 24 p
48 (a) 48 m.p.h.   (b) $1\frac{1}{2}$ h
49 (a) 15 m.p.h.   (b) 40 min
50 60 km/h, $2\frac{1}{3}$ h

Quadratic Equations 2 **12**

1	$-9, 11$	**2**	$-1.16, 5.16$
3	$-1.47, 7.47$	**4**	$-3.42, 11.42$
5	$-4.11, 14.11$	**6**	$-4.45, 0.45$
7	$-7.24, 1.24$	**8**	$-10, 2$
9	$-5.36, 3.36$	**10**	$-2.85, 7.85$
11	$+9$	**12**	$+16$
13	$+36$	**14**	$+25$
15	$+100$	**16**	$+16$
17	$+\frac{9}{4}$	**18**	$+\frac{25}{4}$
19	$+\frac{49}{4}$	**20**	$+\frac{169}{4}$
21	$+\frac{9}{16}$	**22**	$+\frac{25}{64}$
23	$+\frac{9}{49}$	**24**	$+\frac{4}{25}$
25	$+\frac{36}{49}$	**26**	$+1$

27 $-3.41, -0.59$
28 $-4.30, -0.70$
29 $-3, -2$
30 $-3.62, -1.38$
31 $-4.41, -1.59$
32 $-1.14, 6.14$
33 $0.70, 4.30$
34 $1.27, 4.73$
35 $1.70, 5.30$
36 $2, 5$
37 $-5.32, 1.32$
38 $0.44, 4.56$
39 $0.39, 7.61$
40 $-4.30, -0.70$
41 $-9.22, 0.22$
42 $-1.32, 5.32$
43 $-12.25, 0.25$
44 $0.30, 6.70$
45 $1.27, 4.73$
46 $-5.70, 0.70$
47 $-2.35, 0.85$
48 $-0.87, 2.87$
49 $-2.46, -0.54$
50 $-1.34, 0.74$
51 $-1.14, -0.11$
52 $0.30, 1.41$
53 $-1.87, -0.13$
54 $-0.32, 0.62$

55 $-1.65, 0.53$
56 $-0.88, 1.13$
57 $-1.32, -0.11$
58 $-5.65, -0.35$
59 $-9.36, -0.64$
60 $0.88, 9.12$
61 $-2.13, -9.87$
62 $-1.55, 0.22$
63 $-0.24, 1.64$
64 $-0.30, -1.41$
65 $-4.65, 0.65$
66 $-0.31, 0.81$
67 $-5.90, -0.10$
68 $-0.85, -1.94$
69 $-0.94, 0.55$
70 $-1.10, 0.62$
71 $-0.30, 1.83$
72 $-0.32, 1.57$
73 $0.44, 4.56$
74 $-1.08, 2.08$
75 $0.45, 1.55$
76 $-0.81, 0.31$
77 $0.28, 0.88$
78 $-3.68, 2.18$
79 $-1.54, 2.34$
80 $0.67, 2$
81 $x = 5$, parallel sides 5 cm, 7 cm. Distance between them 2.5 cm
82 $n = 24$
83   9, 10, 11
84   4.57 m, 6.57 m
85   7.08 m, 12.07 m
86   5.96 cm, 18.04 cm
87   24 cm
88   12 cm × 18 cm
89   15 cm × 20 cm
90   12
91   7.24 × 5.53 m or 14.47 m × 2.76 m
92   1.44 m
93   After 2 seconds and 4 seconds, on the way up and on the way down
94   6 cm
95   20.49 m

Similar Shapes   13

1

Ratio of lengths	Ratio of areas
2:3	4:9
2:1	4:1
5:2	25:4
3:4	9:16
1:x	$1:x^2$
x:y	$x^2:y^2$
3x:5x	9:25
10:9	100:81
5:4	50:32
2:3	28:63
3y:1	$9y^2:1$
4z:5y	$16z^2:25y^2$

2

Ratio of lengths	Ratio of volumes
3:2	27:8
1:2	1:8
2:3	8:27
5:4	125:64
7:4	343:64
x:y	$x^3:y^3$
4x:3y	$64x^3:27y^3$
5:2	1000:64
x:2y	$x^3:8y^3$
2:1	8:1
3:2	54:16
10:3	7000:189

3 (a) ÷100   (b) × 10 000
    (c) ÷1000   (d) × 1 000 000
    (e) ÷10   (f) × 100

4 (a) 10 km   (b) $1\frac{1}{4}\,\text{km}^2$
    (c) 400 m   (d) $0.7\,\text{km}^2$

5 (a) 16 cm   (b) $19.2\,\text{cm}^2$
    (c) $\frac{1}{25}\,\text{cm}^2$ (d) 2 cm

6 (a) 200 km   (b) 4 cm

7 51.2%

8 (a) $208\frac{1}{3}\,\text{cm}^3$ (b) $31\frac{1}{5}\,\text{cm}$

9 28.64, i.e. 29 bags

10 (a) 15 cm   (b) $107.9\,\text{cm}^3$

11 2.64 m, $39.93\,\text{m}^3$, $21.175\,\text{m}^2$, $11\,\text{m}^3$, $3.8\,\text{m}^2$, 7 cm

12 A and B

13

	Smallest car	Other car
Length	360 cm	432 cm
Tank capacity	6.372 gallons	11.01 gallons
Windscreen area	$0.6\,\text{m}^2$	$0.864\,\text{m}^2$
Width	130 cm	156 cm

14 (a) $125\,\text{cm}^3$ (b) $343\,\text{cm}^3$
15 (a) 7 cm   (b) 11 cm
     (c) 49:81:121
16 (a) 33%   (b) 23%

Nets   14

1 (a) H
   (b) BC
   (c) BCLM
   (d) HIJK
   (e)

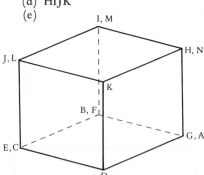

   (f)

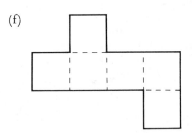

2 (a) $12\,\text{cm}^2$
   (b) $216\,\text{cm}^2$
   (c) $144\,\text{cm}^3$; 20 cm × 16 cm

3 (a) $256\,\text{cm}^3$
   (b) $224\,\text{cm}^2$
   (c) 17.89 cm
   (d) 18 cm

4 (a)

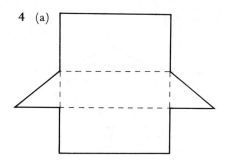

(b)

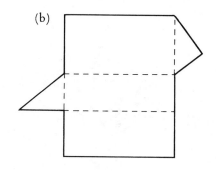

(c)

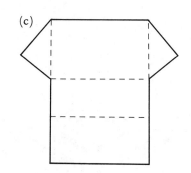

5 (a) F, G and H
(b) E is vertically above B

6 64 cm², 16 cm, 4

7 (a) and (d)

8 (a), (c) and (d)

9 (a)

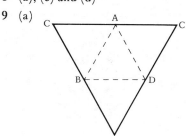

(b) 4.33 cm

10 A hexagonal prism

11 (a)

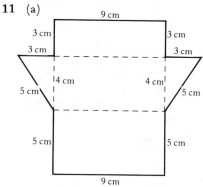

Missing face has four sides.
Could be attached to any
one of these four sides
(b) A triangular prism
(c) (i) 120 cm²   (ii) 54 cm³
(d) (i) and (ii) 9.85 cm

12 (a)

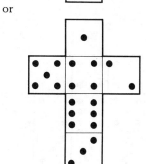

AC = 7.07 cm
(b) 3.54 cm
(c) 29.5 cm³

13 (a) (i)

or

203

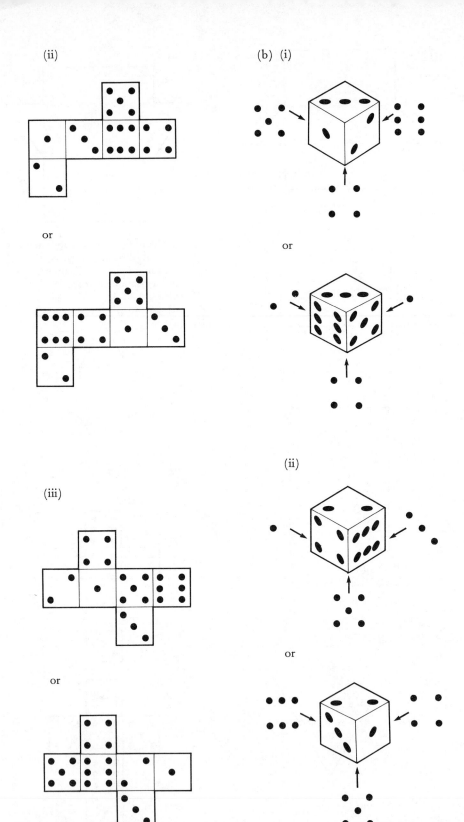

204

Area and Volume　　　　　　　　　　**15**

1　(a)　8 m　　　　　　(b)　£100.80
2　1946 m^2, 0.4865 m^3
3　2000 m, 1000 s
4　2074 cm^2, 21%
5　(a)　312　　　　　　(b)　13
　　(c)　£87.75
6　(a)　15 cm　　　　　(b)　10 cm
　　(c)　250π cm^2　　　(d)　160π cm
7　(a)　3 cm　　　　　　(b)　16 cm
8　(a)　6　　　　　　　(b)　7200 cm^3
　　(c)　5000
9　(a)　155 cm^2　　　　(b)　3162 cm^2
　　(c)　(i)　15 500 cm^3
　　　　(ii)　0.0155 m^3
　　(d)　124 kg
10　(a)　1750 m^3　　　(b)　187.5 m^3
11　(a)　25.13 m　　　　(b)　13.73 m^2
12　(a)　75 m^2　　　　(b)　375 m^2
　　(c)　80 m
13　(a)　13.10 cm, 9.681 cm^2
　　(b)　11.62 cm^3
14　(a)　41 580 cm^3
　　(b)　41.6 litres
　　(c)　109, £26.16, £12.16
15　6870 cm^3

16　(a)　(i)　6 + 2π　　(ii)　3 + π
　　(b)　2 cm
17　(a)　214.6 cm^3　　(b)　261.8 cm^3
　　(c)　82%
18　48%
19　$\frac{2}{3}$
20　(a)　(i)　a　　(ii)　a
　　　　(iii)　1.414a ($\sqrt{2}a$)　(iv)　a
　　　　(v)　1.732a ($\sqrt{3}a$)
　　(b)　5.196 cm
21　(a)　13 m^2　　　　(b)　1.5 m^3
22　18
23　4.64 cm, 21.5 cm^2
24　19$\frac{1}{4}$ cm^3
25　£59.40
26　(a)　5 m　　　　　　(b)　200 m^2
　　(c)　3.2 m^3
27　9.9 cm
28　1152, 18 m^3
29　10
30　1300
31　(a)　484 cm^2　　　(b)　504 cm^3
　　(c)　216 cm^3
32　8 full cups, $\frac{8}{9}$ths cup remains
33　$\frac{370}{3}\pi$ cm^3

Travel Graphs　　　　　　　　　　**16**

1　(a)

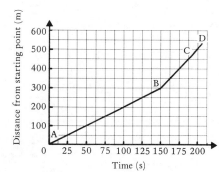

　　(b)　205 s　　　　　(b)　2.61 m/s
2　(a)　(i)　15 km/h　　(ii)　25 km/h
　　(b)　3 h 36 min
　　(c)　The speed suggests a bicycle
3　(a)　(i)　26 m.p.h.　　(ii)　47 m.p.h.
　　(b)　30.8 m.p.h.　(c)　33$\frac{1}{3}$ m.p.h.
　　(d)　57 miles from A at 12.14 p.m.
　　(e)　62$\frac{1}{2}$ miles

4　(a)　56$\frac{1}{2}$ miles from A at 1.46 p.m.
　　(b)　37$\frac{1}{2}$ miles　　(c)　2.14 p.m.
5　(a)　11.36 a.m.　　(b)　50 m.p.h.
　　(c)　67 miles from A at 12.29 p.m.
　　(d)　57 miles
6　(a)　Timothy 2.08 p.m.,
　　　　Colin 1.55$\frac{1}{2}$ p.m.
　　(b)　18$\frac{3}{4}$ miles from D at 1.50 p.m.
　　(c)　3.42 miles
7　(a)　11.39 a.m.　　(b)　12.30 p.m.
　　(c)　2.35 m.p.h.
8　(a)　30 knots, 10 knots
　　(b)　8 a.m. on the second day
　　(c)　321$\frac{1}{2}$ miles from A at 3.09 p.m.
　　　　on the second day
9　(a)　37 m　　　　　(b)　9 m/s
　　(c)　18 m/s　　　　(d)　21 m/s
10　(a)　9 m/s^2　　　　(b)　12 m/s^2
　　(c)　3 s　　　　　　(d)　1$\frac{1}{2}$ s
　　(e)　(i)　36 m　　(ii)　85$\frac{1}{2}$ m

11 (a) (i) 87 m.p.h. (ii) $10\frac{1}{2}$ s
(iii) 105 m.p.h. (iv) 19 s
(b) It gradually reduces over the period
12 (a) (i) 31 m/s (ii) 0.6 m/s^2
(b) At the beginning
(c) 1600 m (to nearest 100 m)

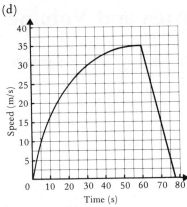

(d)

$17\frac{1}{2}$ seconds
Travels 306 m in this time
13 (a) 15.6 m/s (b) 3.5 m/s^2
(c) 13.7 m (d) 15.6 m
14 (a) 26 s (b) 79 m.p.h.

Circles and Symmetry 17

1 $p = 36°, q = 54°$
2 $r = 55°, s = 35°, t = 55°$
3 $u = 44°, v = 44°$
4 $w = 65°, x = 25°, y = 65°,$
$z = 130°$
5 $a = 90°, b = 74°$
6 $c = 90°, d = 33°, e = 33°$
7 $f = 19°, g = 39°$
8 $h = 45°$
9 $i = 42°, j = 48°$
10 $k = 37°, l = 90°, m = 53°$
11 $p = 62°, q = 28°$
12 $r = 43°, s = 43°, t = 94°$
13 $u = 54°, v = 36°, w = 63°$
14 $x = 28°, y = 62°$
15 $a = 60°, b = 30°, c = 120°,$
$d = 60°$
16 $e = f = 45°$

17 $g = 40°, h = 50°, i = 80°, j = 10°$
18 $k = 45°, l = 45°, m = 45°$
19 (a) 13 cm (b) 22.6°
20 (a) 10.95 cm. (b) 57.4°
21 (a) 10 (b) 8.66 cm
(c) 60°
22 (a) 7.39 cm (b) 9.46 cm
(c) 18.92 cm
23 (a) 17.7 cm (b) 9.39 cm
24 (a) 60° (b) 60°
(c) 55°
25 (a) 9.85 cm, 12.61 cm
(b) 6.30 cm, 4.93 cm
26 (a) 12.8 cm (b) 6.81 cm
27 (a) 17.9 cm (b) 11.4 cm
28 (a) 5.29 cm (b) 10.6 cm
(c) 6 cm (d) 63.6 cm^2

Constructions 18

1 12.5 cm
3 5.46 cm
4 6.5 cm
5 4.3 cm
7 4.2 cm
8 4.9 cm and 16 cm
9 4.8 cm and 8.2 cm
10 4.3 cm and 10.3 cm

11 AD = 6.3 cm, AC = 10.6 cm,
BD = 13.7 cm
12 4.3 cm
13 (a) AB = 4.6 cm
(b) AD = AF = 11.1 cm
14 7.64 cm, $53\frac{1}{2}$ cm^2
15 CD = 7.56 cm
16 9 cm

Probability

19

1 (a) $\frac{5}{26}$ (b) $\frac{1}{13}$ (c) $\frac{7}{26}$
2 (a) $\frac{1}{8}$ (b) $\frac{3}{8}$ (c) $\frac{1}{8}$
3 (a) $\frac{1}{2}$ (b) $\frac{1}{4}$ (c) $\frac{7}{8}$
4 (a) $\frac{1}{2}$ (b) $\frac{5}{12}$ (c) $\frac{11}{36}$
   (d) $\frac{5}{6}$
5 (a) $\frac{1}{17}$ (b) $\frac{16}{17}$ (c) $\frac{4}{17}$
6 (a) $\frac{11}{50}$ (b) $\frac{13}{25}$ (c) $\frac{3}{50}$
   (d) $\frac{2}{25}$ (e) $\frac{12}{25}$ (f) $\frac{1}{25}$
7 (a) (i) $\frac{4}{15}$ (ii) $\frac{11}{15}$ (iii) $\frac{1}{5}$
   (iv) $\frac{4}{5}$ (v) 1
   (b) (i) Simon is a boy
       (ii) Simon has blue eyes
   (c) (i) $\frac{8}{29}$ (ii) $\frac{112}{435}$
8 (a) $\frac{1}{6}$ (b) $\frac{1}{3}$ (c) $\frac{1}{30}$
   (d) $\frac{2}{5}$
9 (a) $\frac{1}{4}$ (b) $\frac{1}{6}$ (c) $\frac{5}{12}$
10 (a) $\frac{3}{8}$ (b) $\frac{7}{8}$

11 (a) $\frac{2}{5}$ (b) $\frac{1}{15}$
12 (a)

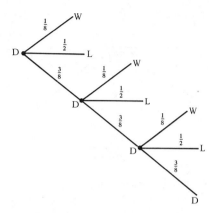

(b) (i) $\frac{3}{64}$ (ii) $\frac{9}{512}$ (iii) $\frac{97}{512}$
    (iv) $\frac{27}{512}$

Statistics

1 (a) (i) 54 (ii) 40 (b) 30%
2 (a) 75 min (b) 1 h
3 (a) £540 000 (b) 79%
4

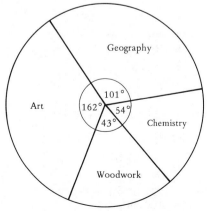

5

6 (a) £50

(b)

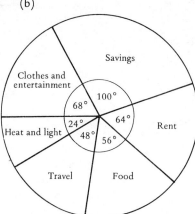

Chart segments: Savings, Clothes and entertainment, Heat and light, Travel, Food, Rent, with central angles 100°, 68°, 24°, 48°, 56°, 64°

7 £59

8 For 1.8, Against 0.6

9 155 cm,

(a) 800 cm

(b) 157.3 cm

10 75

11 Mean 4.62, Mode 3, Median 4

12 Mean 3.58, Mode 6, Median 4

13 Mean £16, Median £13

14 (a) 11   (b) 28   (c) 10

(d) 1   (e) 2.36

15 (a) 103

(b)

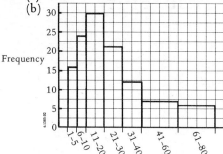

Frequency histogram, Number of cigarettes smoked per day (1-5, 6-10, 11-20, 21-30, 31-40, 41-60, 61-80)

16 (b) (i) 62 kg   (ii) 184 cm

(c) 1.4   (d) 7 kg

(e) F

17 (b) (i) £4   (ii) 325

(c) 75 — the number of pages I can expect for £1

(d) A

18 (b) (i) 420   (ii) 38   (iii) 16

(iv) 27%   (v) 30%

19 (c) (i) £35 500

(ii) £41 000, £31 000

(d) 67%

20 (a) 1201   (b) 14.3 years

(c) 2.9 years

Variation

21

1 (a) $P = kQ$ (b) $H = kt^2$

(c) $y = \dfrac{k}{\sqrt{x}}$ (d) $p = \dfrac{k}{q}$

2 (a) 16   (b) $1\frac{1}{2}$

3 (a) 2   (b) 30

4 (a) 320   (b) ± 5

5 (a) $4\frac{1}{2}$ (b) ± 8

6 (a) 64   (b) $2\frac{1}{2}$

7 (a) 15   (b) 1

8 (a) 9   (b) $\frac{1}{5}$

9 (a) $\frac{27}{8}$ (b) 6

10 (a) $12\frac{1}{2}$ (b) $\pm\frac{8}{3}$

11 (a) 4   (b) 45

12 $\dfrac{a}{b} = -\dfrac{3}{4}$

(a) $\frac{40}{3}$ (b) -3

13 (a) $\frac{1}{2}$

(b) (i) 4   (ii) 16

(c) (i) 25   (ii) $\frac{4}{9}$

(d) $x = \dfrac{y^2}{16}$

14 (a) $-\frac{1}{3}$ (b) $4\frac{1}{2}$

(c) $\frac{8}{27}$ (d) $x = \dfrac{729}{y^3}$

15 (a) $V = 2R^2 H$ (b) $200\,\text{cm}^3$

(c) 3 cm

16 (a) 72 cm of mercury

(b) $400\,\text{cm}^3$

17 1000
18 (a) 216 cm³   (b) 1728 cm³
19 7200 joules
20 80%

21 (a) 2 s   (b) 81 cm
22 120 ohms
23 1.877 years or 685 days
24 (a) 8F   (b) $\frac{1}{8}F$

Trigonometry in Two- and Three-Dimensions

22

1 (a) (i) 5.30 cm
        (ii) 8.48 cm
    (b) (i) 24.6 cm
        (ii) 17.2 cm
    (c) (i) 8.63 cm
        (ii) 8.34 cm
    (d) (i) 4 cm
        (ii) 6.93 cm
    (e) (i) 4.46 cm
        (ii) 4.01 cm
    (f) (i) 4.09 cm
        (ii) 13.4 cm
2 (a) 13.3 cm   (b) 4.70 cm
    (c) 4.85 cm   (d) 9.65 cm
3 (a) 6.68 cm   (b) 8.58 cm
    (c) 32.7 cm   (d) 12.6 cm
4 (a) 15.2 cm, 9.38 cm
    (b) 5.75 cm, 5.56 cm
    (c) 16.0 cm, 14.9 cm
    (d) 8.94 cm, 10.8 cm
5 (a) 31.8°   (b) 5.27 cm
    (c) 22.4 cm²
6 15.1 m
7 40.4 m, 86.6 m
8 100 m, 800 m
9 (a) 5.80 cm   (b) 1.55 cm
    (c) 46.4 cm²
10 (a) 6.14 m   (b) 8.60 m
    (c) 2.46 m, 5.16 m
11 1500 m, 1.07 p.m. (to nearest
    minute)

12 (a)

    (b) 8 n. miles, 3.46 n. miles
    (c) 20 knots
13 (a) 55.7 cm   (b) .24.5 cm
    (c) 0.12 m³
14 17.3 m, AE = 26.0 m, 33.6°
15 (a) 14.1 cm, 14.1 cm, 14.1 cm,
        86.1 cm²
    (b) Tetrahedron
    (c)

16 (a) 31°   (b) 25.1°
    (c) 50.2°
17 (a) 11.3 cm   (b) 90°
    (c) 5.66 cm   (d) 121 cm³
18 (a) 20.7°   (b) 28.1°
    (c) 26.8°

Graphs

23

1 (a) 0 to 5 years and 10 years to
        16 years
    (b) From 7 years to 10 years
    (c) About 18 years
    (d) it will increase
2 (a) Day 2   (b) 37°C
    (c) Day 4
3 (a) 27 mm   (b) 32 g

4 (a) 12.24 p.m. and 5.10 p.m.
    (b) 4.1 m
5 (a) 5.06 a.m.   (b) 18th April
6 (a) 33 cm   (b) 0.44 m²
7 (a) 4.8 m
    (b) 26½ m and 63 m from the bank
    (c) 46½ m

8 (a) 0.44 m or 0.895 m
   (b) 0.252 m², 0.71 m

9 (a) 5.5 and 11.2
   (b) 1300 cm² when $a = 8.6$ (approx.)

10 (a) A$(-2, 0)$, B$(0, -6)$, C$(3, 0)$
   (b) $y \equiv 2x - 6$
   (c) $x^2 - 2x - 3 = 0$

11 (a) $p = 12, q = 1$
   (b) $(0, 12)$

12

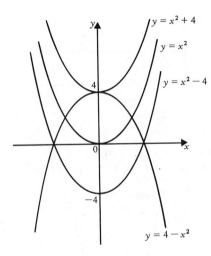

13

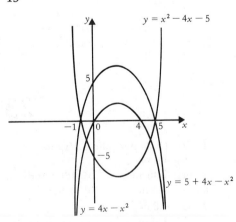

14 (a) $(x - 3)(x - 4)$ (b) 3, 4
   (c) A$(0, 12)$, B$(3, 0)$, C$(4, 0)$
   (d) $x = 3.5$
     $(3.5, -0.25)$

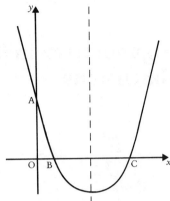

15 (a) $4, -5$ (b) $x = -2$
   (c) $(0, -5)$ (d) -6 and 2
16 (a) $(3 - x)(1 + 2x)$
   (b) $-\frac{1}{2}, 3$
   (c) A$(-\frac{1}{2}, 0)$, B$(0, 3)$, C$(3, 0)$
   (d) $x = \frac{5}{4}$
17 (a) $y = 6, \pm2.45$
   (b) $y = 2x + 6, -1.65, 3.65$
   (c) $y = \frac{1}{2}x + 3, -1\frac{1}{2}, 2$
18 $-7.25, 1.5$
   (a) (i) -1.19 and 4.19
      (ii) -1.70 and 4.70
   (b) -0.45 and 4.45
   (c) from -0.45 to 4.45
   (d) $x^2 - 4x - 2 = 0$
19 (a) graph   (b) $x = \frac{3}{2}$
20 (a) -2.36 and 1.69
   (b) $12\frac{1}{3}$ when $x = -\frac{1}{3}$
21 (a) 4.9 and 15.1
   (b) 43.9 cm²
   (c) 50 cm² when $b = 10$
22 (a) 3.75
   (b) 0.75 and 3.12
23 (a) from 1.27 to 4.73
   (b) 1.27 and 4.73
   (c) $x^2 - 6x + 6 = 0$
24 $6\frac{2}{3}, 3\frac{2}{5}, 3$; from 1.59 to 4.41;
   $x^2 - 6x + 7 = 0$
25 (a) £409   (b) 5.84 knots
   (c) 9.5 knots
26 (a) 48 cm²   (b) 4.8 cm
   (c) 78 cm²
27 0.64, 0.77, 0.34
   (a) 0.82, 0.42   (b) 45°

Loci

1

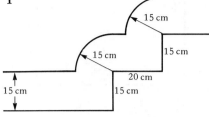

15 cm

15 cm

15 cm

20 cm

15 cm

15 cm

15 cm

2

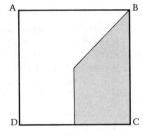

5 cm

M

A

B

N

Radius = $3\frac{1}{8}$ cm

3 (a)

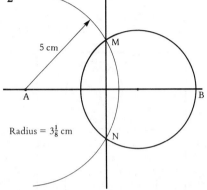

A

B

D

C

(b) $\frac{3}{8}$ area of square i.e. $937\frac{1}{2}$ m^2

4

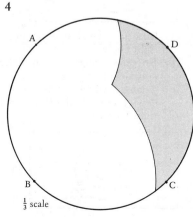

A

D

B

C

$\frac{1}{3}$ scale

5

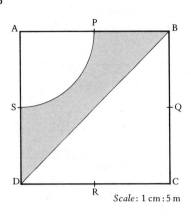

A

P

B

S

Q

D

R

C

Scale: 1 cm : 5 m

6 (a) A circle, centre O, radius 5 cm
(b) A circle, centre A, radius 5 cm
(c) A circle, centre B, radius 8 cm
(d) A circle, centre B, radius 8 cm, in a plane perpendicular to BC

7

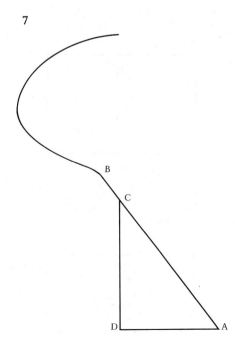

B

C

D

A

Sets

1 (a) $A \cup B = \{2, 3, 4, 5, 6, 7, 8\}$
   (b) $A \cap B = \{2, 4, 6\}$
2 (a) $\{x, y, z\}$ (b) $\{w\}$
   (c) $\{v, w, z\}$
3 (a)

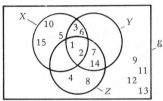

   (b) $\{5, 10, 15\}$
4 (a) $\{2\}$ (b) $\{1, 9\}$
   (c) $\{1, 2, 9\}$
5 (a) $\{6, 8, 10, 12, 14, 16, 18, 20\}$
   (b) $\{6, 9, 12, 15, 18\}$
   (c) $\{6, 12, 18\}$
   (d) $\{9, 15\}$
   (e) $\{5, 7, 11, 13, 17, 19\}$
6

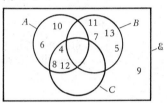

7 (a) $3\frac{1}{3}$ (b) -5
8 (a) $\cos 30°$ (b) $\sin 30°$
9 (a) $\left(\frac{1}{2}\right)^{-3}$ (b) 1
10 (a)

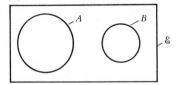

   (b)

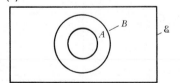

   (c)

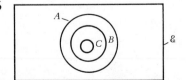

(d)

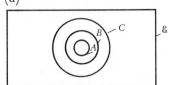

11 (a) 1, 2, 3, 4
   (b) 1, 2, 3, 4, 5, 6, 7
   (c) 6, 7, 8
   (d) 1, 8
12 (a) 11, 12   (b) 5, 6, 7
   (c) 5, 6, 7   (d) 10, 11, 12
13

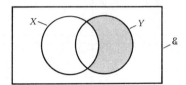

14

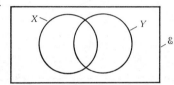

   (a) Natural numbers which are
       multiples of 2 and of 3
   (b) Natural numbers which are
       either multiples of 2 or 3
   (c) Natural numbers which are
       multiples of 2 but not of 3
15

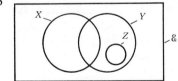

   (a) Isosceles triangles containing a
       right angle
   (b) Isosceles triangles which do not
       contain a right angle
   (c) Triangles which are neither
       isosceles nor do they contain a
       right angle, $\emptyset$
16

(image reference 16)

17 17
18

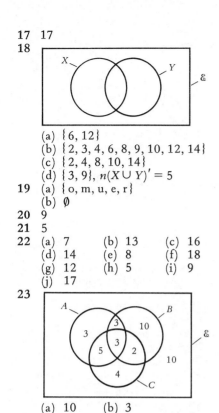

(a) {6, 12}
(b) {2, 3, 4, 6, 8, 9, 10, 12, 14}
(c) {2, 4, 8, 10, 14}
(d) {3, 9}, $n(X \cup Y)' = 5$
19 (a) {o, m, u, e, r}
    (b) ∅
20 9
21 5
22 (a) 7   (b) 13   (c) 16
    (d) 14   (e) 8   (f) 18
    (g) 12   (h) 5   (i) 9
    (j) 17
23

(a) 10   (b) 3

24 (a) {4, 5, 8, 10, 12, 15, 16, 20, 24,
        25, 28, 30}
    (b) ∅   (c) &   (d) **Y**
25 (a), (c) and (e)
26 (a) 40   (b) 27   (c) 24
    (d) 49
27 41, 22
28 (a) 54   (b) 18   (c) 5
29

$x = 11$
(a) 24   (b) 29
30 (a) 3   (b) 6

Determinants and Matrices   **26**

1 14   **2** 17   **3** −37
4 1   **5** 0   **6** 3
7 −54   **8** −33   **9** 442
10 233   **11** −23   **12** 7

13 (a) $\begin{pmatrix} 9 & 5 \\ 6 & 4 \end{pmatrix}$ (b) $\begin{pmatrix} 3 & 4 \\ 3 & 2 \end{pmatrix}$

(c) $\begin{pmatrix} 11 & 9 \\ 9 & 5 \end{pmatrix}$ (d) $\begin{pmatrix} 29 & 14 \\ 21 & 10 \end{pmatrix}$

(e) $\begin{pmatrix} 26 & 19 \\ 18 & 13 \end{pmatrix}$ (f) $\begin{pmatrix} 25 & 18 \\ 18 & 13 \end{pmatrix}$

14 (a) $\begin{pmatrix} -1 & 6 \\ 22 & 22 \end{pmatrix}$ (b) $\begin{pmatrix} -27 & 19 \\ 0 & 22 \end{pmatrix}$

(c) $\begin{pmatrix} 33 & 4 \\ 2 & 44 \end{pmatrix}$ (d) $\begin{pmatrix} -3 & 23 \\ 62 & 6 \end{pmatrix}$

15 (a) $\begin{pmatrix} 25 & 10 \\ 17 & 9 \end{pmatrix}$ (b) $\begin{pmatrix} 43 & 18 \\ 31 & 19 \end{pmatrix}$

(c) $\begin{pmatrix} 15 & 5 \\ 8 & 1 \end{pmatrix}$ (d) $\begin{pmatrix} 93 & 47 \\ 59 & 30 \end{pmatrix}$

(e) $\begin{pmatrix} 92 & 35 \\ 81 & 31 \end{pmatrix}$ (f) $\begin{pmatrix} 79 & 30 \\ 50 & 19 \end{pmatrix}$

16 (a) $\begin{pmatrix} -16 & 28 \\ 20 & -16 \end{pmatrix}$

(b) $\begin{pmatrix} -18 & 10 \\ -4 & 12 \end{pmatrix}$

(c) $\begin{pmatrix} -17 & 19 \\ 8 & -2 \end{pmatrix}$

(d) $\begin{pmatrix} -10 & 5 \\ -2 & 5 \end{pmatrix}$ (e) $\begin{pmatrix} 61 & -83 \\ 38 & -38 \end{pmatrix}$

(f) $\begin{pmatrix} 71 & -15 \\ 6 & 26 \end{pmatrix}$

17 (a) $\begin{pmatrix} -15 & 42 \\ 9 & -5 \end{pmatrix}$

(b) $\begin{pmatrix} 21 & -18 \\ -3 & 11 \end{pmatrix}$

(c) $\begin{pmatrix} 10 & -15 \\ -3 & 5 \end{pmatrix}$

(d) $\begin{pmatrix} -117 & 192 \\ 21 & -28 \end{pmatrix}$

(e) $\begin{pmatrix} 144 & -57 \\ 0 & 49 \end{pmatrix}$

(f) $\begin{pmatrix} 1728 & -831 \\ 0 & 343 \end{pmatrix}$

18 $A^{-1} = \begin{pmatrix} -7 & 6 \\ 6 & -5 \end{pmatrix}, \begin{pmatrix} 1 & 0 \\ 0 & 1 \end{pmatrix},$
$\begin{pmatrix} 1 & 0 \\ 0 & 1 \end{pmatrix}$

19 $X^{-1} = \begin{pmatrix} 1 & -1 \\ -\frac{8}{5} & \frac{9}{5} \end{pmatrix}, \begin{pmatrix} 1 & 0 \\ 0 & 1 \end{pmatrix}, \begin{pmatrix} 1 & 0 \\ 0 & 1 \end{pmatrix}$

20 $M^{-1} = \begin{pmatrix} -\frac{3}{2} & -\frac{5}{2} \\ 1 & 2 \end{pmatrix}, \begin{pmatrix} 1 & 0 \\ 0 & 1 \end{pmatrix}, \begin{pmatrix} 1 & 0 \\ 0 & 1 \end{pmatrix}$

21 $Y^{-1} = \begin{pmatrix} \frac{1}{10} & -\frac{1}{5} \\ -\frac{1}{10} & \frac{8}{15} \end{pmatrix}, \begin{pmatrix} 1 & 0 \\ 0 & 1 \end{pmatrix}$

22 $Z^{-1} = \frac{1}{38} \begin{pmatrix} 4 & 6 \\ 3 & -5 \end{pmatrix}, \begin{pmatrix} 1 & 0 \\ 0 & 1 \end{pmatrix}$

23 $\begin{pmatrix} 48 \\ 39 \end{pmatrix}$ 24 $\begin{pmatrix} 60 \\ -17 \end{pmatrix}$ 25 $\begin{pmatrix} 13 \\ 123 \end{pmatrix}$

Transformations   27

1 $\begin{pmatrix} 3 \\ 1 \end{pmatrix}$ 2 $\begin{pmatrix} 8 \\ -4 \end{pmatrix}, (1, -3)$

3 $\begin{pmatrix} 2 & -4 \\ 3 & 5 \end{pmatrix}$ 4 $\begin{pmatrix} \frac{3}{2} & \frac{5}{2} \\ \frac{1}{3} & -\frac{4}{3} \end{pmatrix}$

5 (a) $\begin{pmatrix} 4 \\ 5 \end{pmatrix}, \begin{pmatrix} 4 \\ -3 \end{pmatrix}$ (b) $\begin{pmatrix} 4 \\ 4 \end{pmatrix}$

6 (a) $\begin{pmatrix} -5 \\ 4 \end{pmatrix}, \begin{pmatrix} 5 \\ 8 \end{pmatrix}$ (b) $\begin{pmatrix} -5 \\ 4 \end{pmatrix}$

7 (a) $\begin{pmatrix} 6 \\ 2 \end{pmatrix}, \begin{pmatrix} -3 \\ -5 \end{pmatrix}$ (b) $\begin{pmatrix} 4 \\ -3 \end{pmatrix}$

8 $O(0, 0), A'(8, 6), B'(6, 8),$
$\triangle OAB = 3\frac{1}{2}$ sq. units,
$\triangle OA'B' = 14$ sq. units,
$\dfrac{\triangle OA'B'}{\triangle OAB} = \dfrac{4}{1}, \ |M| = 4$

9 $(0, 0), (-3, 10), (-6, 14);$
$(0, 0), (5, 4), (-2, 2),$
$M_1 M_2 \neq M_2 M_1$, 9 sq. units;
area preserved under both
transformations

10 (a) $(2, -6), (-22, -24)$

(b) $\begin{pmatrix} \frac{1}{2} & \frac{-1}{3} \\ \frac{1}{2} & \frac{-2}{3} \end{pmatrix}$ (c) $(1, -4$

(d) $\begin{pmatrix} 10 & -2 \\ 3 & 3 \end{pmatrix}$ (e) $\begin{pmatrix} 6 & 0 \\ 0 & 6 \end{pmatrix}$

11 (a) A reflection in the line
$y = -x$
(b) A reflection in the line
$x + y = 3$

12 (a) A reflection in the line
$y = -x$
(b) A reflection in the line
$x + y = 2$

13 (a) $A'(-2, 4), B'(5, 0), C'(10, 0)$
(b) Graph
(c) Rotation of triangle clockwise
about O through an angle θ
where $\tan \theta = \frac{3}{4}$

14 (a) to (c)

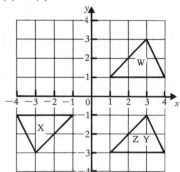

(d) Y and Z are identical
15 (a) and (b)

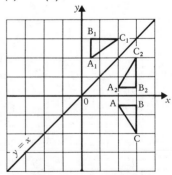

(c) Reflection in the x-axis

16 (a) and (b)

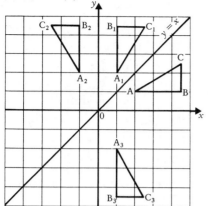

(c) Rotation of the triangle about O through 90° anticlockwise
(d) Rotation of the triangle about O through 90° clockwise
(e) A rotation of 90° clockwise about O

17 (a) and (b)

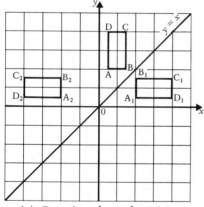

(c) Rotation about the origin through 90° anticlockwise

Vectors

1 (a) $\overrightarrow{CD}$ and $\overrightarrow{PQ}$
(b) $\overrightarrow{GH}, \overrightarrow{LK}, \overrightarrow{EF}$
(c) $\overrightarrow{IJ} = 3\overrightarrow{CD}$

2

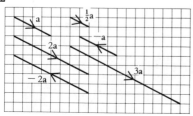

18 A(1, 1)
B(4, 2)
C(3, 5)

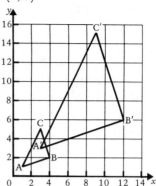

Scale factor 3

19 (0, 3), scale factor 2

20 A(2, 1), B(4, 7), C(6, 3), $\begin{pmatrix} 6 \\ 2 \end{pmatrix}$

21 (a) $\begin{pmatrix} 2 \\ 0 \end{pmatrix}, \begin{pmatrix} 0 \\ -4 \end{pmatrix}$ (b) $\begin{pmatrix} 2 & 0 \\ 0 & -2 \end{pmatrix}$

(c) $\begin{pmatrix} 6 \\ -4 \end{pmatrix}, \begin{pmatrix} -4 \\ 6 \end{pmatrix}$

22 (a) $\begin{pmatrix} -3 \\ 0 \end{pmatrix}, \begin{pmatrix} 0 \\ 3 \end{pmatrix}$ (b) $\begin{pmatrix} -3 & 0 \\ 0 & 3 \end{pmatrix}$

(c) $\begin{pmatrix} -9 \\ 6 \end{pmatrix}, \begin{pmatrix} -6 \\ -9 \end{pmatrix}$

23 (a) $\begin{pmatrix} -1 \\ -2 \end{pmatrix}, \begin{pmatrix} -3 \\ -4 \end{pmatrix}$

(b) $\begin{pmatrix} -1 & 0 \\ 0 & -1 \end{pmatrix}$

28

3

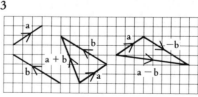

4 $\begin{pmatrix} -4 \\ 7 \end{pmatrix}, \begin{pmatrix} 5 \\ -2 \end{pmatrix}, \begin{pmatrix} -1 \\ -5 \end{pmatrix}$

5 $\begin{pmatrix} 3 \\ 9 \end{pmatrix}, \begin{pmatrix} -4 \\ 8 \end{pmatrix}, \begin{pmatrix} -7 \\ -1 \end{pmatrix}$

6 $\begin{pmatrix} -2 \\ 3 \end{pmatrix}, \begin{pmatrix} 4 \\ 5 \end{pmatrix}, \begin{pmatrix} 6 \\ 2 \end{pmatrix}$

7 (a) $\begin{pmatrix} -6 \\ 4 \end{pmatrix}, \begin{pmatrix} 12 \\ -8 \end{pmatrix}, \begin{pmatrix} 3 \\ -2 \end{pmatrix}$

(b) $\begin{pmatrix} 2 \\ 3 \end{pmatrix}$

8 (a) $\begin{pmatrix} -3 \\ 1 \end{pmatrix}, \begin{pmatrix} 6 \\ -2 \end{pmatrix}$

(b) $\begin{pmatrix} 1 \\ 3 \end{pmatrix}, \begin{pmatrix} -1 \\ -3 \end{pmatrix}$

9 (a) $(5, -4), (-2, 6)$

(b) $-\frac{10}{7}, \begin{pmatrix} 7 \\ -10 \end{pmatrix}$

10 (a) $(2, 4), (4, -4)$

(b) $\begin{pmatrix} -2 \\ 8 \end{pmatrix}$ (c) $(3, 0)$

11 (a) $(2, 6), (2, -4)$

(b) $\begin{pmatrix} 4 \\ -4 \end{pmatrix}, \begin{pmatrix} -4 \\ -6 \end{pmatrix}$, PQRS is a trapezium with QR parallel to PS

12 $(2, 4), (4, -2), (-4, 2)$

13 (a) $\begin{pmatrix} 4 \\ -7 \end{pmatrix}$ (b) -5

(c) $\begin{pmatrix} 11 \\ -3 \end{pmatrix}$

14 (a) $\begin{pmatrix} -4 \\ 1 \end{pmatrix}$

(b) $\begin{pmatrix} 13 \\ 9 \end{pmatrix}, r = 5, s = -3$

15 (a) $\begin{pmatrix} 2 \\ 1 \end{pmatrix}$ (b) $\begin{pmatrix} -8 \\ 10 \end{pmatrix}$

(c) $\begin{pmatrix} -8 \\ 3 \end{pmatrix}$

16 (a) $\begin{pmatrix} 12 \\ 1 \end{pmatrix}$ (b) $\begin{pmatrix} 17 \\ -2 \end{pmatrix}$

(c) $\begin{pmatrix} 1 \\ -\frac{3}{2} \end{pmatrix}$

17 (b) $\mathbf{b} - \mathbf{a}$ (c) $\begin{pmatrix} 3 \\ -3 \end{pmatrix}$

18 (a) $\begin{pmatrix} 6 \\ -3 \end{pmatrix}$ (b) $(-2, 2)$
(c) Parallel

19 (a) $\mathbf{b} - \mathbf{a}$ (b) $\frac{2}{3}(\mathbf{b} - \mathbf{a})$
(c) $\frac{1}{3}\mathbf{a} + \frac{2}{3}\mathbf{b}$

20 (a) (i) $\overrightarrow{CB} = 2\mathbf{x} - 2\mathbf{y}, \overrightarrow{CP} = \mathbf{x} - \mathbf{y}$,
$\overrightarrow{AP} = \mathbf{x} + \mathbf{y}$
(ii) $\overrightarrow{AG} = \frac{2}{3}(\mathbf{x} + \mathbf{y})$
(b) (i) $BQ = \mathbf{y} - 2\mathbf{x}$
(ii) $\overrightarrow{HB} = \frac{2}{3}(2\mathbf{x} - \mathbf{y})$
$\overrightarrow{AH} = \frac{2}{3}(\mathbf{x} + \mathbf{y})$, G and H are coincident

21 (a) $2(\mathbf{b} - \mathbf{a})$ (b) $\frac{1}{2}(\mathbf{b} - \mathbf{a})$
(c) $\frac{1}{2}(\mathbf{a} + 3\mathbf{b})$

22 (a) $2(\mathbf{b} - \mathbf{a})$ (b) $\mathbf{a}$
(c) $\mathbf{b}$ (d) $\mathbf{b} - \mathbf{a}$
PR is parallel to AB and equal to one half of it

23 (a) $\mathbf{p} + \mathbf{q}$ (b) $2\mathbf{q}$
(c) $\mathbf{q} - \mathbf{p}$ (d) $\mathbf{p} - \mathbf{q}$
(e) $2\mathbf{p} - \mathbf{q}$

24 (a) $\mathbf{y}$ (b) $2\mathbf{x} + \mathbf{y}$
(c) $\mathbf{y} - 2\mathbf{x}$ (d) $\frac{2}{3}(\mathbf{y} - 2\mathbf{x})$
(e) $\frac{4}{3}(\mathbf{x} + \mathbf{y})$ (f) $2(\mathbf{x} + \mathbf{y})$.
N lies on AC

25 (a) $\mathbf{x} + \mathbf{y}, 2\mathbf{x} + \mathbf{y}$
(b) $\overrightarrow{AM} = \mathbf{x} + \frac{1}{2}\mathbf{y}, \overrightarrow{AN} = \frac{1}{2}(\mathbf{x} + \mathbf{y})$
(c) $\overrightarrow{NM} = \frac{1}{2}\mathbf{x}$
(d) NM is parallel to CB and equal to one sixth of it

26 (a) $\overrightarrow{AB} = \mathbf{c}; \overrightarrow{CB} = \mathbf{a}$
(b) $\overrightarrow{OM} = \mathbf{a} + \frac{1}{2}\mathbf{c}, \overrightarrow{ON} = \frac{1}{2}\mathbf{a} + \mathbf{c}$
(c) $\overrightarrow{MN} = \frac{1}{2}(\mathbf{c} - \mathbf{a}), \overrightarrow{AC} = \mathbf{c} - \mathbf{a}$
(d) MN is parallel to AC and equal to half of it

27 (a) $\overrightarrow{AC} = \mathbf{c} - \mathbf{a}, \overrightarrow{AM} = \frac{1}{2}(\mathbf{c} - \mathbf{a})$
(b) $\overrightarrow{OM} = \frac{1}{2}(\mathbf{a} + \mathbf{c})$,
$\overrightarrow{MB} = \mathbf{b} - \frac{1}{2}(\mathbf{a} + \mathbf{c})$
(c) $\overrightarrow{MG} = \frac{1}{3}\mathbf{b} - \frac{1}{6}(\mathbf{a} + \mathbf{c})$,
$\overrightarrow{OG} = \frac{1}{3}(\mathbf{a} + \mathbf{b} + \mathbf{c})$

28 $\mathbf{a}, 2\mathbf{b}, 2(\mathbf{b} - \mathbf{a}), \mathbf{b} - \mathbf{a}$,
$\dfrac{\triangle OMB}{\triangle OAC} = \dfrac{1}{4}$

29 (a) $\overrightarrow{AC} = \begin{pmatrix} 6 \\ -4 \end{pmatrix}, \overrightarrow{CB} = \begin{pmatrix} -9 \\ -6 \end{pmatrix}$
(b) $\overrightarrow{AD} = \begin{pmatrix} 6 \\ -3 \end{pmatrix}, \overrightarrow{DE} = \begin{pmatrix} -12 \\ -6 \end{pmatrix}$,
$\overrightarrow{EF} = \begin{pmatrix} 12 \\ -6 \end{pmatrix}$
(c) $\overrightarrow{AB} = \begin{pmatrix} -3 \\ -10 \end{pmatrix}, \overrightarrow{BG} = \begin{pmatrix} 1 \\ -9 \end{pmatrix}$

Functions   29

1 (a) (i) −6   (ii) 60
   (b) (i) 2 and 9   (ii) 0 or 11
2 (a) 3   (b) −7
   (c) 5   (d) $4x − 1$
   (e) $4x − 3$
3 (a) 17   (b) 9
   (c) 47   (d) 289
   (e) −3

4 (a) 13   (b) −5
   (c) −14   (d) −4
5 (a) 27   (b) $\frac{1}{3}$
   (c) 1
6 (a) (i) 9   (ii) −15   (iii) −12
   (b) (i) −6, 2   (ii) 0, −4
      (iii) −2 (twice)
7 (a) 16   (b) $\frac{1}{4}$ (c) $-\frac{1}{2}$

The Sine Rule and Cosine Rule   30

1 (a) 9.745   (b) 37.19
   (c) 7.661   (d) 4.751
   (e) 4.764   (f) 75.94
   (g) 10.24   (h) 15.18
   (i) 68.88
2 (a) 35°   (b) 39.6°
   (c) 45.2°   (d) 69.3°
   (e) 31.4°   (f) 28.4°
   (g) 82.4°   (h) 22.8°
3 (a) $a = 11.4, C = 60°, c = 12.9$
   (b) $b = 27.1, C = 56°, c = 29.3$
   (c) $a = 15.9, B = 47°, b = 11.7$
   (d) $b = 8.97, C = 77.7°, c = 9.77$
4 79.89 m, 200.7 m
5 5.717 n. miles, 11.43 knots
6 2.308 km from A and 3.904 km
   from B
7 (a) 57.18 m   (b) 42.65 m
8 PY = 14.58 km, PQ = 13.92 km
9 AC = 0.9306 km, BC = 0.2292 km
10 (a) 337.6   (b) 545.2
   (c) 42.98   (d) 72.25
11 (a) 4.583   (b) 11.33
   (c) 4.974   (d) 5.639

12 (a) 82.8°   (b) 47.2°
   (c) 81.7°   (d) 48.5°
13 AĈB, 101.5°
14 4.8°
15 165°, 13.88 cm
16 327.5 km in a direction N68.7°E
17 214.7 miles in a direction
   N28.2°W, 23 026 sq. miles
18 249.7 m in a direction N23.5°W
19 AD = 97.62 m, BC = 57.27 m,
   DC = 73.30 m, area = 5196 m²
20 (a) AM = 81.63 m, BM = 342.4 m
   (b) 198.6 m   (c) N23.1°E
21 (a) 31.5 m
   (b) AD = 205 m, BD = 205 m,
      DC = 217 m
   (c) 4.25 hectares
22 (a) 49.0 m   (b) 81.0 m
   (c) 43.3 m   (d) 4170 m²
23 (a) Each edge has a length equal to
      the sum of two radii
   (b) 10 cm   (c) 8.66 cm
   (d) 5.77 cm   (e) 8.17 cm
   (f) 18.17 cm (5 + 8.17 + 5)

Revision Paper   1

1 (a) $3b(2a + c)$
   (b) $(b + c)(a − d)$
   (c) $(x − 3)(x + 2)$
   (d) $(5a + 2b)(5a − 2b)$
2 (a) 1, 2, 3, 4   (b) 5
   (c) 7
3 (a) $13a + 11b$
   (b) $2a^2 + 5ab + 2b^2$
   (c) $−2a + 16b$

4 (a) 3   (b) 5   (c) $\pm\frac{5}{2}$
5 (a) (0, 8)   (b) $y = −2x + 8$
6 John £18, Harry £10.80, Tom £9.60
7 (a) 10   (b) 14
8 (a) 5   (b) $c = \sqrt{a^2 − b^2}$
9 (a) (4, −3)   (b) (8, 21)
10 (a) 48 cm²   (b) 864 cm²
   (c) 1152 cm³

Revision Paper 2

1 £2
2 £77 decrease
3 20°, 18
4 $\frac{50}{3}mx$
5 216
6 £920
7 $k = -5$
8 8 cm²
9 (a) 21   (b) 67
   (c) 30
10 (a) 23 m/s after $27\frac{1}{2}$ s
   (b) 0.52 m/s²   (c) $27\frac{1}{2}$ s

Revision Paper 3

1 (a) 1×10^{10} (b) 4×10^{0}
   (c) 2.5×10^{5} (d) 1.5×10^{5}
2 45°, 8
3 3^4 and 9^2
4 $-3, -2.95, 2.7, 3\frac{1}{2}, 5$
5 $-\frac{3}{4}, 10$
6 Red £2.50, White £2
7 (a) $-2, 5$
   (b)

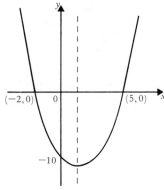

8 (a) $x + y = 40$ (b) $x > 2y$
   (c) $18x + 13y > 500$
9 (a) 640 000   (b) 2 560 000
   (c) 20 000
10 2 m, 124 m

Revision Paper 4

1 (a) 18 500
   (b) 83 500, 84 499
2 £588
3 (a) 5   (b) 4
4 (a) 16, 25
   (b) No, only $x = 25$. Squaring both
        sides introduces a possible error
5 962 cm³
6 $x = 4, y = 5$
7 (a) A$(-4, -3)$, B$(3, 4)$
   (b) (5, 0), (0, 5), $(-5, 0)$, $(0, -5)$
8 £9500
9 (a) 10 m²   (b) 2.5 m
   (c) 5.5 m²   (d) 27.5 m³
   (e) 1 m³
10 (a) 3.4 cm   (b) 87 cm²

Revision Paper 5

1 228
2 131
3 (a) 13   (b) 27   (c) $8\frac{1}{2}$
4 (a) $A = \{3, 6, 9, 12\}$,
    $B = \{4, 8, 12\}$;
    $A \cap B = \{12\}$;
    $(A \cup B)' = \{1, 2, 5, 7, 10, 11$
                   $13, 14\}$
    (b) 9
5 1.92×10^6 years
6 (a) $\frac{7}{10}$ (b) $\frac{4}{15}$

7

8 2 h
9 0.0196 km^2
10 (a) 782 m, 329 m
    (b) 318 m
    (c) 252° or S72°W

Revision Paper 6

1 £24
2 153
3 (a) $85\,000 \text{ cm}^3$ (b) 0.085 m^3
    (c) $68\,000 \text{ g}$ (d) 68 kg
4 3.125p, 3.5p, 16 oz can

5 (a) t (b) $\frac{1}{t}$

    (c) $t^2 - \frac{1}{t^2}$

6 $k = 1$,   (a) 31   (b) 5
7 (a) 5.34 cm
    (b) 4.72 cm, 33.3 cm^3
8 42.5 cm
9 An enlargement, centre O, followed
    by a reflection. Scale factor $\sqrt{5}$
10 (a) 55   (b) 210   8

Revision Paper 7

1 (a) £16   (b) £49
2 $\dfrac{fv}{\sqrt{f^2 - 1}}$
3 (a) 3 cm, 9 cm, 5 cm, 5 cm
    (b) 24 cm^2
4 (a) 45, 37, 29   (b) 153
    (c) $3N - 24$ (d) 53
    (e) Rectangles go outside square
5 (a) 1
    (c) $(0, 6), (6, 0)$
    (d) $y = -x + 6$

6 (a) Yes
    (b) $A = \frac{3}{2}b^2$
    (c) 54
    (d) 10
7 44.8°
8 38.05 miles, S5.4°E (174.6°)
9 An enlargement, centre O, followed
    by a rotation about O.
    Area increased ten-fold
10 7.75 m.p.h.

Revision Paper 8

1 £83.85
2 10.1
3 (a) 64   (b) 8

4 $9.5 \times 10^{12} \text{ km}$
5 8
6 (a) 202

7 (a) $b = 1, c = -20$

   (b) $R = \dfrac{100}{P}(A - P), 16$

8 (a) $1\frac{1}{2}$ hours after the session begins on Thursday morning

(b)

	Monday	Tuesday	Wednesday	Thursday
a.m. p.m.	English Maths	Wood./Cook. Chemistry	Hist./Geog. Physics	French

9 $a = 5, b = 30, 6.2, 3.162$
10 (a) Rotation of $180°$ about O
   (b) Rotation of $180°$ about point $(2, \frac{3}{2})$

Revision Paper   9

1 (a) 8, 1, 2   (b) $\dfrac{3a}{b^3}$

   (c) $-\dfrac{3x + 2}{(2x - 1)(x + 2)}$

2 (a) (i) $\frac{1}{2}(2 - a)(2 + a)$
       (ii) $(3a - 2)(2a + 3)$
   (b) 22   (c) $(y - x)z$
3 (a) $\frac{4}{3}$ (b) ± 6
4 (a) £1345.60   (b) £1160
   (c) £1531.20
5 (a) $-3, 5$ (b) 7
   (c) 6
6 20 lb at 23 p per lb
7 £225
8 -2.36 and 1.69,
   $3x^2 + 2x - 12 = 0$
9 (a) 7, 8, 9; 21, 32, 45; 28, 32, 36
   (b) $n + 4, n(n + 4), 4(n + 4)$
   (c) 117
   (d) 2

10 (a)

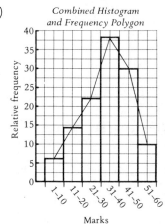

Combined Histogram and Frequency Polygon

(b)

Mark	≤10	≤20	≤30
Cumulative frequency	6	20	42
Mark	≤40	≤50	≤60
Cumulative frequency	80	110	120

   (i) 80   (ii) 78   (iii) $\frac{7}{20}$

(c) (i) 35   (ii) 43, 25   (iii) 20
    (iv) 24

Revision Paper 10

1 5056 drachma, £26.06
2 82.4 km
3 (a) 25:16   (b) (i) $-\frac{4}{5}$,   (ii) 0
4 (a) (i) 25   (ii) 1   (iii) 125
   (iv) 1
   (b) $\dfrac{8}{a^3 b^2}$ (c) $4a^2 b^2$
5 (a) 11   (b) $(11, -22)$
   (c) $\begin{pmatrix} \frac{1}{11} & -\frac{2}{11} \\ \frac{3}{11} & \frac{5}{11} \end{pmatrix}$ (d) $(3, 5)$
   (e) $\begin{pmatrix} 19 & 12 \\ -18 & -5 \end{pmatrix}$
6 (a) (i) 126   (ii) 58
   (b) $4x + 18$ (c) 22
   (d) (i) 29   (ii) 2
   (e) (i) No whole number x so that
        $4x + 18 = 43$
      (ii) Triangle would go outside
        the number square
7 Via B, 0.315 km
8 (a) 1.25 m   (b) 1.27 m
   (c) 29.6°   (d) 37.4°
   (e) 22 400 cm^3
9 (a) $(0, 0), (-7, 0), (0, 4)$
   (b) $(-3, 6), (\frac{1}{2}, 2\frac{1}{2})$
10 (a) 30.5 miles from Boxley at
      1.37$\frac{1}{2}$ p.m. and 69 miles from
      Boxley at 3.22$\frac{1}{2}$ p.m.
   (b) 3.07$\frac{1}{2}$ p.m.   (c) 4.24 p.m.

Revision Paper 11

1 19 200
2 (a) £61 000   (b) £41 000
3 (a) 43
   (b) $\dfrac{2s}{u + v}$
4 $(6, 6)$
5 $C = 8n$, the cost of one unit of
   electricity
6 0.046 mm
7 (a) 36 n. miles   (b) 111 n. miles
   (c) 109$\frac{1}{2}$ n. miles
8 (a) 39°   (b) 12°   (c) 78°
9 $\begin{pmatrix} 2 & 4 \\ 1 & 3 \end{pmatrix}$, $(0, 0), (2, 1), (6, 4), (4, 3)$
   Area = 2 sq. units, $|M| = 2$
10 8.5°, 2.8°

Revision Paper 12

1 (a) 2028   (b) £9464
2 $-\dfrac{(b + c)}{(a + b)}, \dfrac{(a - c)}{(a + b)}$
3 $A = \frac{3}{2}r^2$
4 (a) 2   (b) 20
5 (a) (i) -10 (ii) -18
   (b) (i) $-2, 9$ (ii) $0, 7$
   (iii) $3, 4$
6 (b) 2 sq. units, 18 sq. units
   (c) 9   (d) 9 (same as (c))
7 59 650
8 (a) KC = 7.228 m
   (b) 29°   (c) 30.3°
9 (a) 3 s   (b) 3   (c) -9
10 3

Revision Paper 13

1 (a) by £1.20
2 48π, 0.19 cm
3 (a) 12 (b) 55 (c) 15
4 (a) 18.7 knots, £14.97
   (b) £17.70 (c) 12.9 knots
5 1 0 8 9
   2 1 7 8
   3 2 6 7
   4 3 5 6
   5 4 4 5
   6 5 3 4
   7 6 2 3
   8 7 1 2
   9 8 0 1

6 (a) 29.6 cm
   (b) 34.2 cm
   (c) 17.1 cm

7 (a) 117 m
   (b) 62 m and 76 m
   (c) 116 m

8 66 m

9 (a) 29
   (b) 3.3 and 7.3
   (c) 32, 5.66

10 $(-\frac{3}{2}, -2)$, $(2, \frac{3}{2})$

Revision Paper 14

1 (a) 2387 (b) 6750
   (c) 81 min
2 200π
3 (a) 199 (b) 156
4 (a) (i) 9 (ii) 1 (iii) 9
   (b) $a = 3$, $b = -9$, no, yes
5 -19
6 (a) $\frac{1}{12}$ (b) $\frac{5}{36}$

7 (a) 4.42 p.m. (b) 9.4 miles
   (c) 5 min (d) 4.40 p.m.
8 450, £6.75
9 4.74 m, 115.5 cm², 0.4 m³, 5
10 (a) $5 + 11 + 17$
    (b) $7 + 13 + 41$
    (c) $13 + 31 + 47$

Revision Paper 15

1 0.2 m, 27% (to nearest whole number)

2 (a) £4.95 (b) 4.5%
   (c) £19.80

3 $x = 14$p, $y = 30$p

4 (a) When $t = 8$
   (b) When $t = 2$ and 6
   (c) When $t = 4$
   (d) (i) 4 unit/s (ii) 0

5 (a) 2 (b) 2 (c) -1
   (d) 3 (e) 2

6 (a) (3, 3), (1, 5)
   (c) Rotation anticlockwise through
        45° about the origin, followed
        by enlargement, centre O, scale
        factor $\sqrt{2}$
7 (a) $38\frac{1}{2}$ m s⁻¹ when $t = 22\frac{1}{2}$ s
   (b) $16\frac{1}{2}$ s and $29\frac{1}{2}$ s
   (c) 2.2 m s⁻²
8 (a) 130 m (b) 95.2 m²
9 (a) 8.1 m (b) 4.6°
   (c) 5.1°
10 $k = 4$

Revision Paper 16

1 £756
3 £103.50
4 (a) 39°, 141°   (b) 13.3 cm
  (c) 28.3 cm^2
5 (a) 11.3 cm   (b) 1010 cm^3
  (c) (i) 603 cm^2 (ii) 75%
6 (a) Graph
  (b) (i) -2.4 m s^{-2} (ii) 57 m
7 (a) $\frac{10}{23}$ (b) $\frac{3}{23}$ (c) $\frac{2}{23}$

  (d) $\frac{1}{46}$ (e) $\frac{1}{23}$ (f) 0
8 (a) $\frac{5}{9}$ (b) $\frac{5}{18}$ (c) $\frac{1}{6}$
  (d) $\frac{5}{18}$ (e) $\frac{5}{18}$ (f) $\frac{5}{9}$
9 (a) 0   (b) 7   (c) 48
  (d) $4x^2 + 8x - 65$
  (e) 3, -5
  (f) $-2.32, 4.32$
10 (a) (i) 45.5   (ii) 61, 28, 33
  (b) (i) $\frac{11}{15}$ (ii) $\frac{1}{15}$

Revision Paper 17

1 (a) -0.9563 (b) 47.1°
  (c) 40.2°
2 (a) $1\frac{3}{5}$ (b) $4:5$
3 -0.55 and 0.26
4 (a) 34.7°   (b) $d = \sqrt[3]{\dfrac{MkT^2}{4\pi^2}}$
5 (a) $25:49$ (b) $125:343$

6 (a) $2\frac{1}{4}$ (b) ±5
7 (a) 4   (b) 2
8 (a) (i) 24   (ii) -4
  (b) (i) $-7, -2$ (ii) $-9, 0$
  (iii) $-8, -1$
9 $\begin{pmatrix} 1 & 3 \\ 0 & 1 \end{pmatrix}$, Yes
10 BC = 3 cm, AE = 4.7 cm

Revision Paper 18

1 (a) 2   (b) 4   (c) 8
2 (a) 21   (b) 10
3 25 cm
4 (a) A(2, 1), B(4, 1), C(2, 5)
  (b) (i) $\begin{pmatrix} 2 \\ 0 \end{pmatrix}$ (ii) $\begin{pmatrix} -2 \\ 4 \end{pmatrix}$
  (c) (i) Reflection in $y = -x$
    (ii) Rotation of 180° about O
  (d) Reflection in $y = x$
5 300π (approx.)
6 £42
7 (a) $\frac{12}{51}$ (b) $\frac{13}{51}$ (c) $\frac{3}{51}$
  (d) 0

8 (a) 35 000 miles
  (b) Every 7000 miles
  (c) $\begin{smallmatrix} 1 & 3 \\ 4 & 2 \end{smallmatrix}$ 5   If this is the original position with 5 indicating the boot the changes could be:

    $\begin{smallmatrix} 5 & 2 \\ 3 & 1 \end{smallmatrix}$ 4, $\begin{smallmatrix} 4 & 1 \\ 2 & 5 \end{smallmatrix}$ 3, $\begin{smallmatrix} 3 & 5 \\ 1 & 4 \end{smallmatrix}$ 2

    and $\begin{smallmatrix} 2 & 4 \\ 5 & 3 \end{smallmatrix}$ 1

9 (a) 6   (b) 4
  (c) A regular tetrahedron
10 (a) (i) 3.2   (ii) 1.1
  (c) 1.1 and 5.4
  (d) 1.11 and 5.39

Revision Paper 19

1 (a) $\frac{1}{6}$ (b) 1   (c) 3
2 (a) 6   (b) $\frac{4}{5}$
3 (a) (i) 108 (ii) 293
   (b) $x, x-9, x-18, x-8, x-7,$
   (c) 57, 48, 39, 49, 50
   (d) 8, 9, 80, 81
   (e) (i) No whole number value of
       x satisfies $5x-42=106$
     (ii) The shape goes outside the
       number square
4 21°
5 (a) −1.16, 5.16
   (b) −0.41, 2.41
   (c) $31\frac{1}{4}$

6 $S = \dfrac{x}{22} + \dfrac{y}{13}$, 75
7 (a) $\dfrac{mx}{f}$ (b) $\pounds\dfrac{32f}{7x}$
8 (a) 48 cm²   (b) 4.8 cm
   (c) 78 cm²
9 (a) AF = 171.3 m, BF = 690.0 m
   (b) MF = 403.4 m, N22.4°E
10 (a) 2, 7, 16, 27, 10, 1
   (b) 2, 9, 25, 52, 62, 63
   (c) (i) 71.5 kg,
     (ii) 74.5 kg, 68.2 kg, 6.3 kg
   (d) $\frac{4}{63}$

Revision Paper 20

1 (b) (i) $-\frac{3}{2}$ m s⁻²   (ii) 72 m
2 (a) £8.64   (b) £17.28
   (c) £55.68
3 5.7
4 42
5 (a) 185.0 m   (b) 95.28 m
   (c) 61.42 m
6 (a) (i) (6, 0), (6, 4)
     (ii) (0, 6), (−4, 6)
   (c) $\begin{pmatrix} 0 & -2 \\ 2 & 0 \end{pmatrix}$
   (d) the same   (e) $\begin{pmatrix} 1 & 0 \\ 0 & -1 \end{pmatrix}$

7 (a) $(-\sqrt{3}, 0), (\sqrt{3}, 0), (0, 2),$
    $(0, -3),$ (b) $(-\frac{5}{3}, \frac{1}{3}), (0, 2)$
8 (a) 26 m²
   (b) 28.1 m² when $x = 15$, $x = 15$,
     (i) 18 m²   (ii) 13 m²
9 $3\frac{1}{2}$ m.p.h.
10

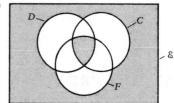

Two pupils went to a cinema and
to a disco

Revision Paper 21

1 England 156 and 468, Australia
  259 and 312
2 $1\frac{1}{6}$ m s⁻¹, $2\frac{32}{49}$ or 2.653 laps
3 (a) 6.428 cm
   (b) 8.87 cm
   (c) 64.4°
4 (a) 4 s   (b) 1   (c) −11

5 (a) 504 km
   (b) 96 km and 504 km
6 $\dfrac{13\,458}{6729} = 2$, $\dfrac{14\,865}{2973} = 5$
7 (b) $w = \frac{1}{2}(n+1)(n+2),$
    $r = 4(n+2)$
   (c) (i) 45 (ii) 56
   (d) 7

8 (a) 8 cm × 12 cm × 25 cm
 (b) 2400 cm³
9 (a) 62
 (b) $n, n-1, n-6$
 (c) 53

(d) (i) No whole number satisfies
   $3n - 7 = 138$
  (ii) Gives a value outside the
    square

10 (a) 1:9   (b) 4:9

Revision Paper   22

1 $\dfrac{x(100 + p)}{a - b}$

2 (a) 7.5 km
 (b) (i) 1.21 km²   (ii) 121 hectares
3 £30.40
4 (a) £(N + 4M)   (b) $C = N + Mx$
 (c) £$\frac{4}{5}$(N + 7M)
5 (a) 0.22 and 2.28 (b) −1.27 and 2.77

6 (a) 51.3°   (b) 124.2°
 (c) 36.8°
7 (a) (i) 36   (ii) ±$\frac{1}{2}$
 (b) 16
8 $x = 3$ (a) 7   (b) 6
9 40 m.p.h.
10 (a) 0.057 m s⁻² (b) $\frac{1}{9}$ m s⁻²
 (c) 11.0 km

Revision Paper   23

1 (a) (i) $(3x + 2)(x - 1)$
   (ii) $3x(3x - 1)$
 (b) $k = 7$ (c) −1.16, 5.16
2 (a) 0.625 p   (b) 26 hours
3 (a) 75°   (b) 90°, 43°, 47°
4 (a) 6   (b) (i) 20   (ii) 57
5 (a) (i) $\frac{9}{16}$″   (ii) $\frac{11}{16}$″
 (b) (i) $\frac{3}{16}$″   (ii) $\frac{11}{16}$″
 (c) 15   (d) $\frac{1}{2}$″   (e) $\frac{11}{16}$″
 (f) $\frac{9}{16}$″   (g) 23   (h) 15 mm
 (i) 20 mm   (j) 10 mm, larger
6 (a) (i) $\overrightarrow{OP} = \frac{2}{3}\mathbf{a}$ (ii) $\overrightarrow{PA} = \frac{1}{3}\mathbf{a}$
   (iii) $\overrightarrow{AB} = \mathbf{b} - \mathbf{a}$
   (iv) $\overrightarrow{AQ} = \frac{2}{3}(\mathbf{b} - \mathbf{a})$
   (v) $\overrightarrow{PQ} = \frac{1}{3}(2\mathbf{b} - \mathbf{a})$

 (b) $\overrightarrow{OR} = \overrightarrow{OP} + \overrightarrow{PR}$ i.e.
   $\overrightarrow{OR} = k\mathbf{b} = \dfrac{2}{3}\mathbf{a} + \dfrac{m}{3}(2\mathbf{b} - \mathbf{a})$
   ∴ $m = 2$ for $\mathbf{a}$ to vanish

7 (a) (i) 43   (ii) 18
 (b) (i) −6, 0   (ii) −4, −2

8 £296.40, £50.40

9 Passes first cyclist 30 miles from A
 at 2.15 p.m.
 Passes second cyclist 23 miles from
 A at 2.08 p.m.

10 (c) (i) £92   (ii) 30

Revision Paper   24

1 House £52 900, car £14 450
2 20°, 9
3 (a) 2.4 m s⁻²   (b) 198 m
4 (a) 5 km
 (b) (i) 1 500 000 m²
   (ii) 150 hectares

5 (a) 6.128 m, 7.067 m
 (b) 68°   (c) 8.892 m
6 (a) $\dfrac{60}{x}, \dfrac{60}{x + 20}$
 (b) $x^2 + 20x - 12\,000 = 0, \frac{1}{2}$ s

7 (a) $\frac{1}{36}$ (b) $\frac{1}{12}$ (c) $\frac{1}{4}$
   (d) $\frac{1}{12}$ (e) $\frac{1}{12}$

8 (a) Reflection in y-axis
  (b) Image points are $(-1, 3)$, $(0, 5)$, $(-5, 5)$
  (c) $y = 2x$
  (d) Reflection in $y = 2x$

9 (a)

x	1	2	3
$\dfrac{x^2}{2} + \dfrac{2}{x}$	2.5	3	5.17

(d) 0.88, 2.46
(e) 0.88 and 2.46
   A cubic will have 1 or 3 roots. Another solution is therefore expected.

10 C, (a) $60°$ (b) $38°$

Aural Test   1

1	18 027	2	6, 2
3	6	4	£2.40
5	A rectangle (or square)		
6	105	7	1:9
8	8:27	9	$72°, 72°, 108°$
10	1	11	£3

12	24 m	13	$40°$
14	$\frac{3}{2}$	15	10 cm
16	61	17	$2\frac{1}{2}$
18	2 pounds	19	£31.50
20	1335		

Aural Test   2

1	48	2	12
3	2.51	4	1.2
5	2.065 m	6	4
7	3	8	75 431
9	40 miles	10	2 m
11	5 p.m.	12	5449

13	4 m		
14	10 pupils and 20 pupils		
15	2	16	80
17	£64	18	3:2
19	No	20	21

Aural Test   3

1	132	2	$\frac{1}{2}$
3	8	4	5400 mm^2
5	21 cm	6	Yes
7	$75°, 105°, 105°$	8	$65°, 118°$
9	30	10	2 miles
11	One	12	30%

13	80	14	60
15	£14	16	1.4×10^{-2}
17	The cone	18	9p
19	9 years 4 months		
20	3 h 40 min		

Aural Test 4

1 3078	**2** 0.36		
3 6	**4** 8, 6 cl		
5 £33	**6** $4y - 3x$		
7 72 m.p.h.			
8			

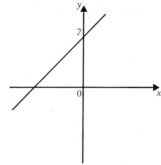

9 4 : 9	**10** £250
11 $7\frac{1}{2}$ h	**12** £95
13 40%	**14** 4 p.m.
15 65 years	**16** 2 m
17 $7\frac{1}{2}$ h	**18** 15 h 20 min
19 11, 12, 13	**20** 22

Aural Test 5

1 1800	**2** 0.6
3 40 miles	**4** Yes
5 2.7 cm^2	**6** 57 cm
7 24 : 16	**8** 40 m.p.h.
9 165	**10** 0230
11 1600	**12** 4 cm
13 4	**14** 40%
15 £4	**16** 8
17 95 320	

18

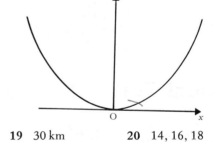

19 30 km   **20** 14, 16, 18

Aural Test 6

1 £45	**2** 30 800
3 8	**4** £9.10
5 38%	**6** 0.42
7 369	**8** 27
9 67%	**10** 30 miles
11 £68.40	**12** $\frac{2}{3}$

13 Yes	**14** 12 km/h
15 2	**16** £1.20
17 15, 17, 19	**18** £3.52
19 12, 24	
20 2, 3, 5, 7, 11, 13	

Aural Test 7

1 96 cm^2	2 $\frac{7}{16}$	13 24	14 6
3 16	4 8 cm	15 26	16 $\frac{3}{7}$
5 75	6 3	17 17	18 4
7 3 cm	8 8	19 Due north	
9 0.24 m	10 238	20 50 kg for £3.30	
11 12 min	12 $4x$		

Aural Test 8

1 5	2 30°	11 £2.20	12 24
3 9 cm	4 0.25	13 150 g	14 £4000
5 18	6 £20.25	15 270 m	16 15
7 $\frac{2}{5}$	8 360°	17 1000 or 1200	18 36 cm^2
9 1 h 25 min	10 1.7 km	19 £1.20	20 $\frac{4}{5}$

Aural Test 9

1 £36	2 1120 g	13 83 years	14 4
3 32 cm	4 340	15 13 weeks	16 11 s
5 22	6 12	17 7, 8, 9	18 4
7 65%	8 18 cm	19 An infinite number	
9 90	10 £2	20 £23	
11 55°	12 6 cm or 5 cm		

Aural Test 10

1 3900	2 20%	11 £11.20	12 52 cm^2
3 12	4 27 cm	13 56	14 5 h
5 $1\frac{7}{8}$	6 $\frac{3}{13}$	15 £6	16 5 cm
7 3 a.m.	8 34	17 0.4	18 322°
9 14 Feb	10 £17.40	19 12	20 2